THE SECRETS OF BUILDING A PLASTIC INJECTION MOLDING MACHINE

Written and Illustrated by
Vincent R. Gingery

David J. Gingery Publishing LLC
P.O. Box 318
Rogersville, MO 65742

Web: http://www.gingerybooks.com
Email: gingery@gingerybooks.com

Printed in the U.S.A.

First printing 1997
Second printing 1998
Third printing 2001
Fourth printing 2003
Fifth printing 2005

Library of Congress
Catalog Card Number
97-94129

International Standard Book Number
1-878087-19-3

TABLE OF CONTENTS

TABLE OF CONTENTS

TABLE OF CONTENTS

WARNING: THERE ARE SERIOUS HAZARDS IN THE PROCESSES AND PROCEDURES IN THIS BOOK. NO ATTEMPT HAS BEEN MADE TO POINT OUT ALL OF THE DANGERS OR EVEN A MAJORITY OF THEM. THE METHODS AND MATERIALS THAT ARE SUGGESTED IN THIS MANUAL WERE DEVELOPED BY A NON-PROFESSIONAL. THE AUTHOR IS NOT AN ENGINEER OR SCIENTIST AND NO CLAIM IS MADE TO THE PROPRIETY OF THE METHODS SUGGESTED IN THESE PAGES. THE READER IS FULLY RESPONSIBLE FOR DEVISING SAFE PROCEDURES FOR EVERY OPERATION.

INTRODUCTION

The purpose of this book is to make available in the simplest of terms, basic knowledge needed to produce small plastic items in the home shop by means of *injection molding*. Injection molding is a process where heat-softened plastic material is forced from the cylinder of an injection molding machine into the cavity of a mold. The liquid plastic cools and hardens in the mold cavity taking the shape of the cavity.

Sources for plastic will be those things normally thrown away. Stuff like plastic milk jugs, soda pop bottles, plastic oil cans etc. In fact, now might be a good time to start saving your plastic throw away stuff. Be sure to rinse out the jugs, particularly the milk jugs. It doesn't take long for milk to sour, and cutting into a milk jug with soured milk is a disgusting thing to say the least. **Do not** save or use containers that have contained chemicals or insecticides. Trace elements of harmful substances will remain on the plastic and could be absorbed through the skin or create harmful fumes when the plastic is melted.

You'll be amazed at how much plastic can be accumulated. In just a short time we had a garage full of the stuff. In all different colors, sizes and shapes too. It certainly proves the value of recycling because all of this stuff would have been thrown away. And besides, plastic takes many hundreds if not thousands of years to decompose. So the question becomes, why put it in a land fill if something useful can be made out of it?

Included in this book are plans to build a small inexpensive table top injection molding machine capable of injecting up to 1/2 ounce of plastic into a mold. You will also learn how to make a simple mold to test the machine. Then a plastic knob will be needed for the adjustable table on the machine so you'll make a mold for that. Then progress to a mold for a small plastic container with a snap lid. It won't be long before you are creating new products of your own design. I'll even show you how to cast replacements for broken or missing plastic parts. You'll soon discover that the possibilities are endless.

Most of the plastic parts around us have been created by huge automated plastic molding machines capable of producing many hundreds if not thousands of parts in a single hour. The injection molding machine you are getting ready to build from the plans in this book will not be the right equipment if you intend to produce parts in great quantity. It is however very appropriate for small jobs. And it's an excellent way to learn the fundamentals of the injection molding process as well as the skills needed to make molds. Keep in mind that all of the parts you see around you started somewhere. Most likely in a

Our injection molding machine.

Fig. 1

7

Simple mold and the items it made.

Fig. 2

small design shop with a small table top injection machine much like the one you will be building. And remember, you've got something exciting to look forward to . . . The raw material that will go into your custom made parts is free. The country is buried in discarded plastic. It's everywhere and in all different colors so with a little effort and the help of this book you can begin your own, very unique, recycling system.

HOW INJECTION MOLDING IS DONE

The process of injection molding plastic is really very simple. I'll describe the operation as it would happen in our machine. And you can study the drawings in **figures 3 through 5** to help you understand the process a little better. Keep in mind that not all machines are alike. But they all have the same purpose and that is to melt plastic and force it into a mold to form a specific part or item. Not all machines are hand operated. Some are air driven while others may use a hydraulic ram. On the larger commercial machines softened plastic is

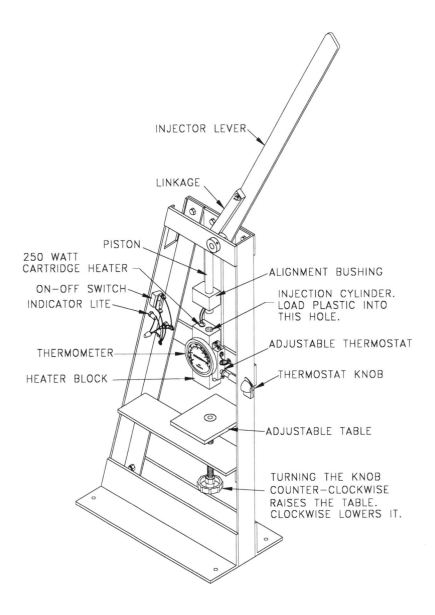

INJECTOR LEVER

LINKAGE

PISTON

250 WATT
CARTRIDGE HEATER

ON-OFF SWITCH
INDICATOR LITE

THERMOMETER

HEATER BLOCK

ALIGNMENT BUSHING

INJECTION CYLINDER.
LOAD PLASTIC INTO
THIS HOLE.

ADJUSTABLE THERMOSTAT

THERMOSTAT KNOB

ADJUSTABLE TABLE

TURNING THE KNOB
COUNTER-CLOCKWISE
RAISES THE TABLE.
CLOCKWISE LOWERS IT.

Fig. 3

9

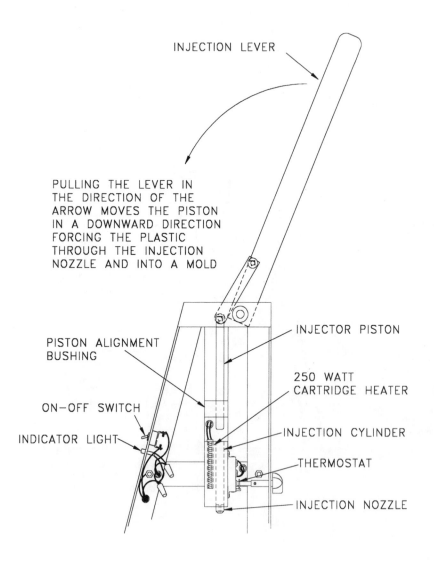

INJECTION LEVER

PULLING THE LEVER IN
THE DIRECTION OF THE
ARROW MOVES THE PISTON
IN A DOWNWARD DIRECTION
FORCING THE PLASTIC
THROUGH THE INJECTION
NOZZLE AND INTO A MOLD

INJECTOR PISTON

PISTON ALIGNMENT
BUSHING

250 WATT
CARTRIDGE HEATER

ON—OFF SWITCH

INDICATOR LIGHT

INJECTION CYLINDER

THERMOSTAT

INJECTION NOZZLE

Fig. 4

10

forced into the mold by a screw ram.

The first step in the operation of our machine would be to load the injection cylinder with plastic material. The injection cylinder is the 1/2" diameter hole located at the top of the heater block. In industry the plastic material is usually in granular form, but in our case we'll be using scrap plastic cut into strips 3/8" to 1/2" wide.

The machine is turned on and the cartridge heater begins heating the plastic in the cylinder. The thermometer keeps us informed of the cylinder temperature as it rises and the temperature is controlled by the thermostat. Proper molding temperatures for plastic will vary depending on the type of

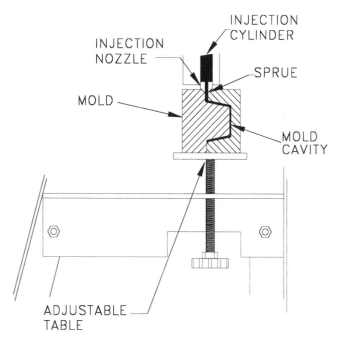

Fig. 5

plastic being used. But more often than not the molding temperature will be somewhere around 400 degrees.

Of course the injection molding machine is of little value without a mold. Molds used in injection molding usually consist of two halves, but there are many possible mold designs and some complicated parts may require multiple piece molds. A simple 2 piece mold and the items it produced is shown in **figure 2**.

Notice in **figure 4** that the injector nozzle has a tapered end. On our machine the taper is 45 degrees. The sprue opening of the mold has a matched 45 degree tapered inset. Since the injection system exerts very high pressure on the mold, the mold halves must be clamped together tightly to prevent the mold from separating and ruining the part during the molding process.

Once the mold is securely clamped together it is placed on the adjustable table. The sprue opening in the mold is aligned with the injector tip. The table is adjusted up forcing the sprue opening tight against the injector tip. As soon as the plastic reaches the proper temperature and is soft enough to flow the injector lever is pulled forward. This causes the piston to plunge down forcing the softened plastic through the injector nozzle and into the mold cavity. After cooling the mold is separated and the part is removed from the mold.

A YOUNG INDUSTRY

Forming objects in molds such as casting metals, blowing glass and shaping clay is ages old, but the plastics industry is relatively new on the scene. The industry was founded on the molding of natural plastics. One example of a natural plastic substance is rubber. For many years rubber was considered a curiosity. Many people attempted to use it for various purposes, but its inability to withstand even moderate temperature changes made it impossible to form anything permanent. Then in 1839 Charles Goodyear discovered vulcanizing. His discovery showed that by treating rubber with sulfur or sulfur compounds in varying proportions and at different temperatures one could increase its strength and elasticity. Depending on the method used either hard or soft rubber could be produced.

Some 50 years later in 1868 the first synthetic plastic was produced by John W. Hyatt. He was a printer by trade and his driving motivation was to produce an ivory substitute for billiard balls. His hope was to win a large prize that had been offered. The poor guy didn't win the prize, but the thermoplastic material that he produced called cellulose nitrate was of much greater use than that which he sought. It has been used for many purposes such as windows in early automobiles, toys and novelties and film for motion pictures. It's problem was that it was highly flammable and as time went on it was gradually replaced by plastic materials that didn't burn as easily.

In 1909 the plastics industry really got a shot in the arm when Dr. Leo Baekeland introduced a new thermosetting resin called phenol formaldehyde later given the name Bakelite. It could be molded using heat and pressure to produce high heat resistant products such as coffee pot handles, pan handles and electrical outlet plugs.

In 1927 a thermoplastic material called cellulose acetate was introduced triggering the rapid development of other plastic resins and forming methods. The result is, that today we have hundreds, if not thousands of plastic materials to choose from.

WHAT IS PLASTIC?

Modern plastics refer to a broad range of synthetic materials. Synthetic materials consist of artificial resins produced by the chemical reaction of organic substances. They are pliable and capable of being shaped by pressure. An important distinction between plastic materials are those that are *thermoplastic* and those that are *thermosetting*.

Thermoplastic refers to those plastics that are capable of being repeatedly softened by heat and hardened by cooling. These are the types of plastic that we can use in our projects.

A few examples of thermoplastics are, *polyvinyl* (introduced in 1927). Its definition covers a broad group of materials used to produce a variety of items ranging from hard rigid products to a soft flexible material. Examples would be seat covers, shower curtains, rain coats etc. Rigid applications would be chemical storage tanks, gutters, siding for houses and blown bottles. *Acrylic* is a thermoplastic material discovered in 1936. Acrylics are known for their exceptional clarity and light transmission. Some acrylic items would be, windows, canopies for boats and aircraft, skylights, lenses, automotive tail lights etc. *Polystyrene,* discovered in 1938 is used for disposable products such as picnic utensils, food containers and novelties. It has outstanding insulative qualities so picnic coolers and jugs are often made from it. *Polyetheline* (introduced in 1942) is the thermoplastic material we will be using a lot of. Two major applications of polyethylene are blow molded bottles and films for packaging soft goods and other non perishables. The above are only a few examples of thermoplastic materials. There are many others.

Thermosetting refers to those types of plastics that can only be hardened by the administration of heat, ultraviolet light or a catalyst. Once these plastics have become set or molded into a given shape they cannot be reheated and reshaped. This means for our recycling purposes thermosetting materials cannot be used.

A few examples of thermosetting materials are *epoxies,* often used for mold making and tools. In fact, we will be discussing the use of aluminum filled epoxy to make molds later in the book. *Melamine*, (Dishes are often made of melamine). *Phenol resins* are commonly used in higher temperature and strength applications such as home appliance handles and parts. Other uses for phenol resins would be distributor caps, coil tops, phone housings and tool housings to name a few.

IDENTIFYING TYPES OF PLASTIC

There are many different types of plastic all having different physical characteristics and chemical composition. An entire book could be written on this subject alone. But our real interest is in whether the plastic will melt in our machine or not.

We know that thermoplastics can be remelted and that thermoset plastics cannot so all we have to do is decide which is which. Thermoset plastics are hard and brittle and it won't be long before you will be able to determine which is which simply by a visual inspection. But if you are uncertain, a good way of making a determination is to heat the end of a metal rod with a torch and touch it against the plastic. If the plastic softens or melts it's thermoplastic and we can use it. If it doesn't melt, it's a thermoset and we can't use it. It's as simple as that.

There are other tests that can be done such as a burn test to determine the exact type of plastic you're dealing with. One example would be, if you were to burn polypropylene or polyethylene the smell would be similar to burning paraffin and the flame would be blue with a yellow top and with polypropylene there would be some white smoke. Most of the plastic throw away bottles you find will be made of polyethylene or polypropylene. It's really not necessary to complicate the issue any more than that. What we are concerned with is, will the plastic material melt, and if so, what is its molding temperature?

DESIGN CONSIDERATIONS

When I first became interested in plastic molding I looked into the possibility of purchasing a machine to do the job for me. Small table top machines could be bought, but they were expensive and for my experimental needs the cost couldn't be justified.

Then it occurred to me that a hot glue gun might work. So off to the shop I went to cut some plastic strips. I stuffed the plastic strips in the chamber of the hot glue gun normally reserved for the glue stick, plugged the gun in the electrical outlet and waited. The gun heated up, but the temperature never got hot enough to melt plastic. Of course the next step was to dismantle the glue gun and see how it worked and if changes could be made to modify it for my purpose. The thing was simple enough. It contained a small casting with a bored cylinder hole for the glue stick. Another bored hole was located next to the glue cylinder and it contained the heater cartridge. And of course there was the trigger mechanism that forced the softened glue through the cylinder and out the nozzle. After a quick examination I became convinced that the glue gun could not be modified to melt plastic. But disassembling it was a good training exercise and it's always fun to take something apart and see what makes it tick even if you can't get it back together again.

From the lessons learned from dismantling the hot glue gun I realized there were four hurdles to overcome before I could build a fully functional injection molding machine. The first challenge was how to heat the injection cylinder. Then there was the matter of determining the temperature of the cylinder at any given moment and figuring out a way to control the temperature. And last, but not least, a way of forcing the softened plastic into a mold cavity.

My goal in any project is to use items that are easily found in the scrap pile or at the local hardware store. So off to the shop I went to see what I could dig up. In my prototype machine the heater problem was solved by using the heating element from a 120-watt Weller® soldering iron. (This wasn't in the scrap pile, it was in my tool box). The proper temperature to inject plastic is usually somewhere between 300 to 400 degrees. A $4.99 oven thermometer has the proper temperature range, and with a small modification it served the purpose. And I learned that it was possible to control the temperature level of the injection cylinder with an adjustable rheostat. (The same type as would be used to dim your living room lights). With the above mentioned items and some angle iron for the frame, I was able to build a functional injection molding machine.

From the very start the project was and continues to be a lot of fun and it wasn't long before I wanted to make improvements to the original machine. Although the soldering iron element worked fine, it's rating of 120 watts meant that it took quite a while to heat the cylinder to its proper temperature. The

17

adjustable rheostat worked fine too once the ideal setting was found. But the drawback here was that the adjustable rheostat works by controlling the amount of voltage supplied. Lower settings on the rheostat decrease voltage and in doing so decrease the wattage rating of the heating element. When new plastic was added to the cylinder it caused a temperature drop and because of the lower voltage it took quite a bit of time to reheat the cylinder.

With a little research I found that the rheostat could be replaced with a 250-600 degree adjustable thermostat. I also found that it was possible to purchase cartridge heaters cheaper than I could buy a soldering iron. As a result, the second generation molding machine works even better than I could have imagined. When the thermostat calls for voltage, full voltage is supplied to the heater and that, coupled with a 250-watt cartridge heater gives the machine a rapid heat up cycle. All in all the original machine worked fine, but it was slow. Simply put, by using the higher wattage cartridge heater instead of the soldering iron heater and a thermostat instead of a rheostat I was able to dramatically increase the operating efficiency of the machine.

Cartridge heaters and thermostats of the type I used are available, but they are tough to find in small quantity lots and impossible to find in the local hardware store. Since these are not easy to find items I felt it best to stock a quantity for those of you who decide to build the machine. The cartridge heaters cost about the same as a soldering iron ($24.95 at the time of the publication of this book). Thermostats cost a bit more than an adjustable rheostat, but are well worth it. ($29.95 at the time of this publication). Ordering information concerning these items can be found at the back of the book.

MATERIALS NEEDED TO BUILD THE INJECTION MOLDING MACHINE

What follows is a short discussion on the materials needed for the project and then a complete material list. As you can see from the drawing in **figure 3** the machine is of a simple design. The frame is made of 1/8" x 1-1/2" x 1-1/2" hot roll steel angle, 3/16" x 2-1/2" x 2-1/2" H.R.S. angle and some 1/4" x 1-1/2" H.R.S. flat bar. The heater block is made from a 4" length of 1" x 1-1/2" cold roll steel bar stock. The injector piston is made from 1/2" C.R.S. round rod. The terms cold roll steel (C.R.S.) and hot roll steel (H.R.S.) refer to the way steel is processed. The surface finish on cold roll steel is smooth and its size is accurate to .003"-.005" when it leaves the mill and is used for more exacting work. Hot roll steel is much cheaper to buy than cold roll steel and its surface finish tends to be rough and scaly. Hot roll steel is ideal for general purpose work such as the frame of our machine.

The best place to purchase the steel angle and flat bar you will need for this project is at a steel yard or scrap yard. At the steel yard ask if you can look through the drops. Drops refer to the left over material that companies often have. These are short ended pieces that really can't be used on other jobs and therefore companies are often more than happy to sell them to you at scrap prices. Avoid cut off fees. These are fees charged to cut pieces of material to length. Most places are likely to charge more for the cut off fee than for the material itself. If you find a piece of material longer than what you need, buy the whole thing and take it home and cut it to length yourself. Add what's left to your scrap pile. It's bound to come in handy on the next project. Often the lumber yard, hardware store or farm supply store will have a rack with an assortment of angle iron and flat bar for sale. The prices are usually higher at these places, but if you can't find it elsewhere they are a good place to look. There are several companies that sell metal products such as angle, flat bar and other items by mail order. I have listed the names, addresses and phone numbers of some of these companies at the back of the book.

The injection molding machine operates on 120 volts. An 18 gauge or heavier power cord with a ground lead and at least 6' long is needed. A 120 volt, 5 amp toggle switch is used to turn the machine off and on and an indicator light lets you know when the heater is in operation. These items can be purchased at the local electronics or hardware store.

A 250-watt cartridge heater 3/8" in diameter and 3" long is used to heat the heater block. A 250-600 degree adjustable thermostat is used to control the temperature of the cylinder block and is mounted to the side of the block. As mentioned earlier in the book, the cartridge heater and thermostat are not going to be found at the hardware store. For information on how you can purchase these items check sources at the back of the book.

A standard oven thermometer with a temperature range of 100 to at least 500 degrees is attached to the front of the heater block and displays the surface temperature of the block. This item can be found in the kitchen drawer or at the grocery store or variety store. Other hardware items such as nuts, bolts, washers etc. are easy to find at the hardware store and are itemized in the material list.

MATERIAL LIST

2-pieces of 3/16" x 2-1/2" x 2-1/2" H.R.S. angle 12" long for the base of the frame. Figure 8 & 9.

1-piece of 1/8" x 1-1/2" x 1-1/2" H.R.S. angle 25-1/8" long for the front post. Figure 10.

1-piece of 1/8" x 1-1/2" x 1-1/2" H.R.S. angle 24" long for the rear post. Figure 11.

2 pieces of 1/4" x 1-1/2" x 6-1/4" H.R.S. flat bar for top braces. Figure 12 & 13.

1-piece of 1/4" x 1-1/2" H.R.S. flat bar 8-3/4" long for the center cross brace. Figure 14.

1-piece of 3/16" x 2-1/2" x 2-1/2" H.R.S. angle 9-5/8" long for the stationary work base. Figure 17.

1-piece of 1/4" x 1-1/2" H.R.S. flat bar 11-1/4" long for the heater post. Figure 18.

1-piece of 1/4" x 1-1/2" H.R.S. flat bar 19" long for the injector lever. Figure 20

2-pieces of 1/4" x 3/4" H.R.S. flat bar 4-1/2" long for the links. Figure 21.

MATERIAL LIST CONTINUED

2-pieces of 1/4" C.R.S. round rod 1" long for linkage pins. See figure 22.

1-piece of 1/2" C.R.S. round rod 3" long for the handle shaft. Figure 23.

1-piece of 1/2" C.R.S. round rod 7" long for the injector piston. Figure 24.

1-piece of 3/8-16 threaded rod 4-1/2" long for the adjustable work table assembly. Figure 28.

1-piece of 1/4" x 3" C.R.S. flat bar 4" long for the adjustable work table. Figure 29.

1-3/8-16 nut for the adjustable table assembly.

1-Plastic knob for the table assembly. (we will make this ourselves)

1-piece of 1" x 1-1/2" C.R.S. bar stock 4" long for the heater block. Figure 32.

1-piece of 1" x 1-1/2" C.R.S. bar stock 1" long for the injector piston alignment bushing. Figure 35.

1-piece of 1/2" C.R.S. round rod 1" long for the injector nozzle. Figure 33. The extra length of this item is needed for mounting in the lathe chuck.

MATERIAL LIST CONTINUED

1- 100-500 degree oven thermometer. Figure 40.

1- 250 watt cartridge heater measuring 3/8 diameter x 3" long. Figure 43.

1-250 to 600 degree adjustable thermostat with knob. Figure 44.

1-piece of 3/8" C.R.S. round rod 1-3/4" long for the thermostat extension shaft. Figure 47.

1- 5 amp/120 volt toggle switch. Figure 48.

1- 120 volt red neon indicator light. Radio Shack #272-712. Figure 48.

2 feet of 14 gauge, 450 degree centigrade (852 degrees fahrenheit) appliance wire.

1- 6' long, 18 gauge 120 volt power cord with ground.

2- 18-12 porcelain wire nuts.

1 piece of 1-1/2" x 3-1/8", 20 gauge sheet metal. Figure 55.

1 piece of 3-3/8" x 7", 20 gauge sheet metal. Figure 56.

1 piece of 2-3/4" x 10", 20 gauge sheet metal. Figure 57.

MATERIAL LIST CONTINUED

1 piece of 1/2" x 3" x 10", 20 gauge sheet metal. Figure 59.

10, 1/4-20 x 3/4 bolts.

9, 1/4-20 nuts and lock washers.

3, 1/4-20 x 1/2 bolts.

6, #10 flat washers.

Four, 6-32 x 3/4 screws.

One, 1/8" x 1/4" rivet.

Two, 8-32 x 1/2" machine screws with nuts.

One, 8-32 x 3/4" machine screw with nut.

4- 1/2" shaft collars.

4- 1/16 x 3/4 cotter pins.

2- 1/4" flat washers.

TOOLS AND CONSTRUCTION METHODS

Building and assembling the frame of the injection molding machine is relatively simple. A hand hacksaw or metal cutting bandsaw is used to cut the material to size. A drill press and an electric hand drill along with a set of drill bits from 1/16" - 1/2" are used for the drilling operations. A good quality 8-32, 1/4-20 and a 3/8-16 tap will be needed. A .501 chucking reamer is needed to finish the injection cylinder bore and a .374 chucking reamer is used to finish the bore for the cartridge heater. Most of the frame will be bolted together, but the right side top brace and right side base require welding so a welder capable of working at 75 amps is needed. You will need an oxy-acetylene torch to braze the threaded shaft to the adjustable table and the injector nozzle to the heater block. A level is needed to align the frame before final assembly and an adjustable protractor is used to check angles. Vise grips or C-clamps are used to hold the frame together during construction.

A metal lathe equipped with a 3 and 4-jaw chuck is needed to face off and bore the heater block and the alignment bushing. It will also be used for a number of other operations as well as mold making. The lathe I used has a 9" swing, but a smaller lathe would work as well.

I'm sure many of you do not own a lathe so an alternative might be to drill and ream the holes in the heater block and alignment bushing using a drill press. If you use a drill press, care must be taken to align the work with the spindle. The work must also be securely mounted to the drill table to prevent it from moving during the drilling operation. Use the best possible drill bits and operate the drill press at a lower speed of around 150 rpm.

BUILDING THE FRAME

Figure 6 shows the front and right side view of the injection molding machine. **Figure 7** shows the rear and left side view. Study the drawings in advance to get a better idea of what

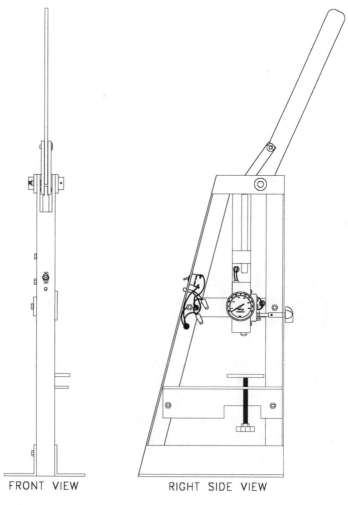

FRONT VIEW   RIGHT SIDE VIEW

Fig. 6

you're getting ready to build. The frame portion of the machine will be built first. The next several drawings will detail each part of the frame followed by an exploded view with labeled parts so you can see what is what and how it all goes together.

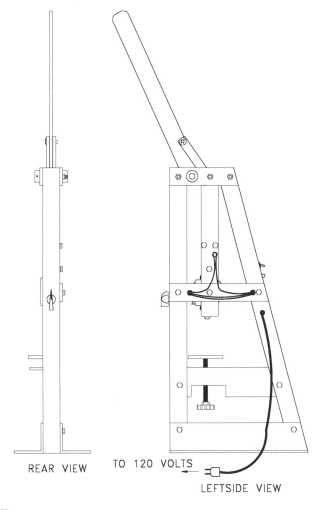

REAR VIEW

TO 120 VOLTS

LEFTSIDE VIEW

Fig. 7

27

Begin the project by making the base rails shown in **figure 8 & 9**. They are an opposing pair and each is made from a 12" length of 3/16" x 2-1/2" x 2-1/2" H.R.S. angle. Cut the 75 degree end on each rail and drill the 1/4" holes in each where shown in the drawings. Notice that the left side base rail has four 1/4" holes while the right side only has two. The extra

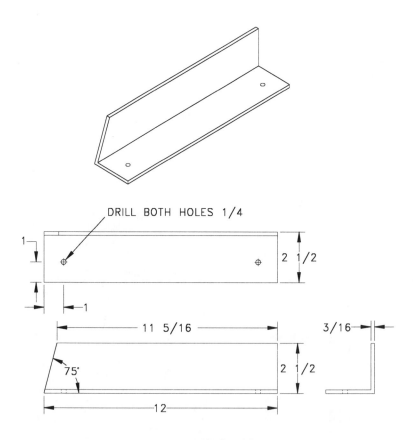

Fig. 8 **Right side base. Made from 3/16" x 2-1/2" x 2-1/2" H.R.S. angle.**

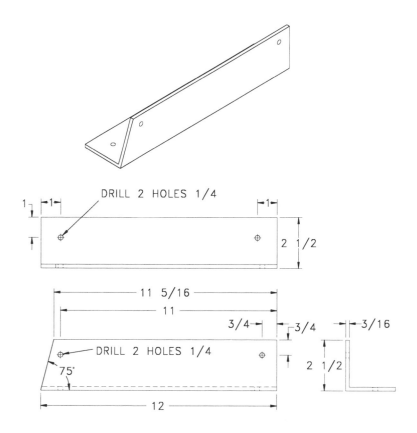

Fig. 9   **Left side base. Made from 3/16" x 2-1/2" x 2-1/2" H.R.S. angle.**

holes in the left side are for bolting the base rail to the front and rear post. The holes are not needed in the right side base rail because it will be welded to the frame.

The front post shown in **figure 10** is made from a 25-1/8" length of 1/8" x 1-1/2" angle. The 75 degree angled ends are checked with an adjustable protractor. The four 1/4" holes are

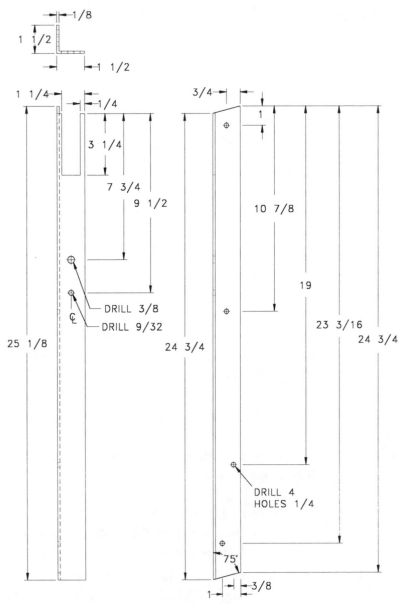

Fig. 10 Front post. Made from 1/8" x 1-1/2" x 1-1/2" H.R.S. angle.

30

for assembling the frame. The 9/32" hole is for the neon indicator light and the 3/8" hole is for the on/off switch. The 1" wide cut out section will give clearance for the injector lever during operation. The perspective view of the front post can be seen in **figure 10A on page 31**.

Make the rear post shown in **figure 11** from a 24" length of 1/8" x 1-1/2" angle. Locate and drill the holes as shown. A perspective view of the rear post can be seen in **figure 11A on page 31**.

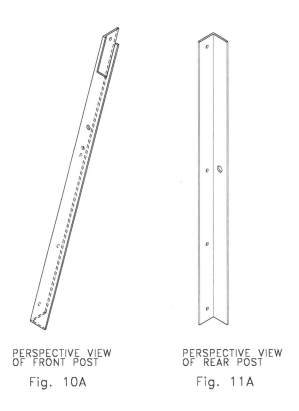

PERSPECTIVE VIEW
OF FRONT POST

Fig. 10A

PERSPECTIVE VIEW
OF REAR POST

Fig. 11A

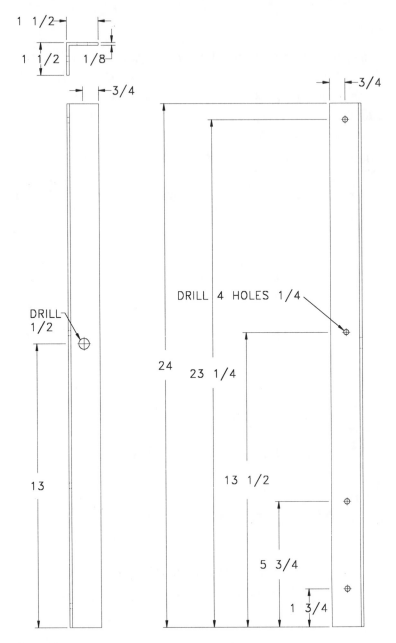

Fig. 11 Rear Post. Made from 1/8" x 1-1/2" x 1-1/2" H.R.S. angle.

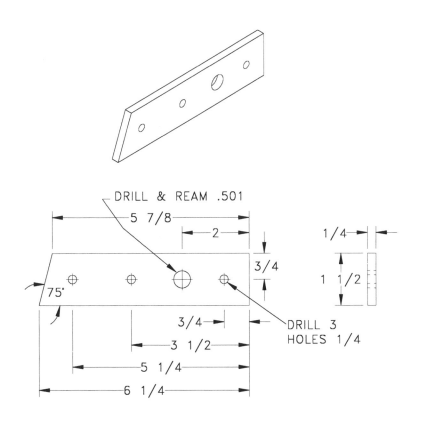

Fig. 12 Left side top brace, made from 1/4" x 1-1/2" H.R.S. flat bar.

The top braces shown in **figure 12 and 13** are each made from a 6-1/4" length of 1/4" x 1-1/2" flat bar and are an opposing pair.

Cut the 75 degree angle end on each brace and drill three 1/4" holes in the left side brace in the locations shown. Two of the 1/4" holes are used to bolt the brace to the frame rails. The heater post will bolt to the top brace using the third 1/4" hole.

To insure that the .501 reamed holes in the right and left brace align with each other clamp the two together and drill & ream through both at the same time.

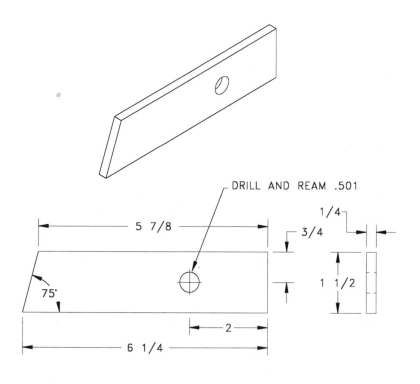

Fig. 13 **Right side top brace, made from 1/4" x 1-1/2" H.R.S. flat bar.**

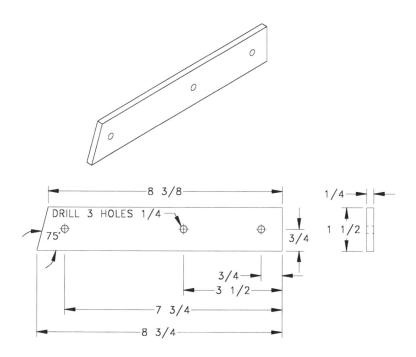

Fig. 14 Center cross brace, made from 1/4" x 1-1/2" H.R.S. flat bar.

The center brace shown in **figure 14** is made from a piece of 1/4" x 1-1/2" H.R.S. flat bar 8-3/4" long. Cut the 75 degree angle end, then locate and drill three 1/4" holes in the locations shown.

We are ready to assemble the parts that have been made so far. The exploded drawing showing the assembly is in **figure 15**. The right side top brace and the right side base are not shown is this drawing because they will be welded to the frame at a later time. All of the pieces are assembled with 1/4-20 x 3/4

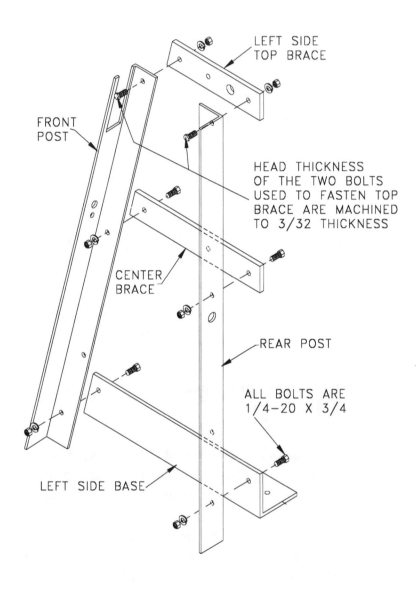

LEFT SIDE TOP BRACE

FRONT POST

HEAD THICKNESS OF THE TWO BOLTS USED TO FASTEN TOP BRACE ARE MACHINED TO 3/32 THICKNESS

CENTER BRACE

REAR POST

ALL BOLTS ARE 1/4–20 X 3/4

LEFT SIDE BASE

Fig. 15

bolts with nuts and lockwashers and you will need 6 of each.

Begin the frame assembly by placing the left side base on a level work bench. Secure the base to the bench with a couple of screws. Loosely attach the front and rear post to the base with the 1/4-20 x 3/4" bolts.

Loosely attach the center cross brace to the front and rear post with 1/4-20 x 3/4" bolts.

Reduce the head thickness of two 1/4-20 x 3/4" bolts to 3/32".These will be used to fasten the left side top brace to the frame. This can be done in

Fig. 16 Squaring the frame

the lathe. Simply chuck the bolt shaft in the 3-jaw and reduce the thickness of the bolt head to 3/32". Then loosely assemble the left side top brace to the front and rear post using these bolts. Note that the bolt heads are located inside the frame with the nuts and lockwashers for the top brace on the outside the frame. The thinner bolt heads allow clearance for the linkage.

For the machine to operate correctly it is important that the frame be built square. You can use a level to square the frame. Of course to get an accurate reading the frame must be on a level table. Place the level against the rear post as shown in

37

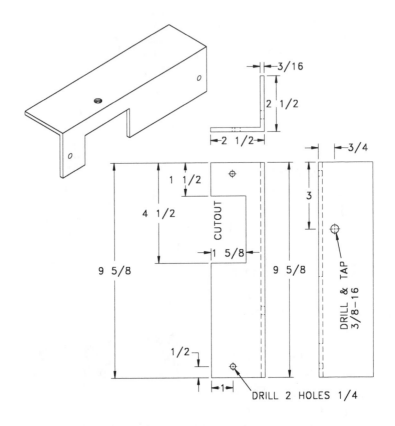

Fig. 17 Work base, made from 3/16" x 2-1/2" x 2-1/2" H.R.S. angle.

figure 16. When you are satisfied with the position of the rear post, tighten all of the bolts. If everything has been assembled properly the left side top brace will also be level. Check to be sure.

The work base is shown in figure 17. Make it from a 9-5/8" length of 3/16" x 2-1/2" H.R.S. angle. Locate and drill the two 1/4" mounting holes. Locate, drill and tap the 3/8-16 hole for the threaded shaft on the adjustable table. The proper drill size for the 3/8-16 tap is 5/16". The 1-5/8" deep x 3" wide cut out

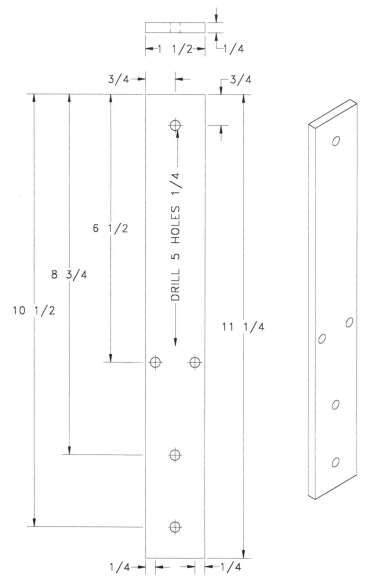

Fig. 18 **Heater post, made from 1/4" x 1-1/2" H.R.S. flat bar.**

39

is needed for clearance for the knob that will be mounted on the end of the screw shaft on the adjustable table.

Make the heater post shown in **figure 18** from a 11-1/4" length of 1/4" x 1-1/2" H.R.S. flat bar. Locate and drill the six 1/4" holes.

Bolt the work base and heater post to the frame using 1/4-20 x 3/4 bolts with nuts and lockwashers as shown in **figure 19**. Reduce the head thickness of the 1/4-20 x 3/4" bolt used to fasten the heater post to the top brace to 3/32".

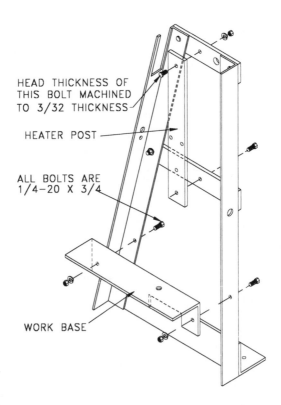

HEAD THICKNESS OF THIS BOLT MACHINED TO 3/32 THICKNESS

HEATER POST

ALL BOLTS ARE 1/4-20 X 3/4

WORK BASE

Fig. 19

THE INJECTOR ASSEMBLY

The injector assembly consists of the injector lever, linkage and piston. Begin by making the injector lever shown in **figure 20**. Make it from a 19" length of 1/4" x 1-1/2" H.R.S. flat bar. A bench grinder can be used to form the 1/2" radius on the handle end. Locate, drill and ream the .251 and .501 holes.

Make two links as shown in **figure 21**. They will be a matching pair. Make each one from a 4-1/2" length of 1/4" x 3/4" H.R.S. flat bar. To insure a matched pair clamp the two links together and drill the holes through both at the same time. Grind a 1/4" radius on one end of each link.

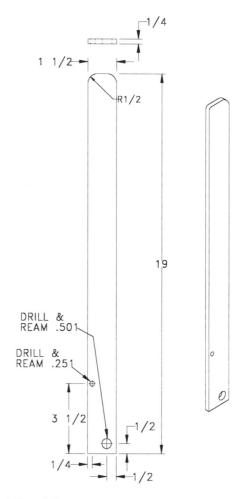

Fig. 20 Injection lever, made from 1/4" x 1-1/2" H.R.S. flat bar

41

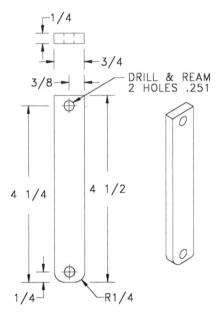

Fig. 21 Links, made from 1/4" x 3/4" H.R.S. flat bar. Make a matched pair.

The linkage pins shown in **figure 22** are made from 1/4" C.R.S. round rod and are 1" long. Drill a 5/64" hole in each end for cotter keys. When drilling small holes in round rod it is best to clamp the work securely in a V-block. Mark the hole location with a center punch. There is always the danger of breaking

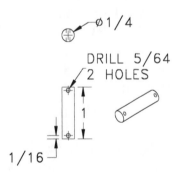

Fig. 22 Linkage pin, made from 1/4" C.R.S. round rod. Make 2

42

a drill bit when drilling small holes in round rod. To reduce the risk, back the drill out several times while drilling to clear it of loose chips. Then proceed carefully through to finish the hole.

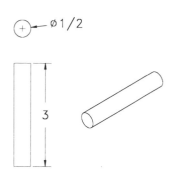

Fig. 23 **Injector lever shaft, make from 1/2" C.R.S. round rod**

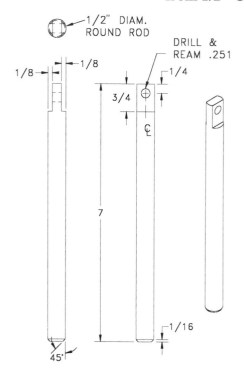

The lever shaft is simply a 3" length of 1/2" C.R.S. round rod and is shown in **figure 23**.

The injector piston is made from a 7" length of 1/2" C.R.S. round rod. A drawing of it is shown in **figure 24**. The 1/8" deep flats on the end of the piston can be made with a file, or you could use a bench grinder to rough them out and then finish with a file. Of course if you have a milling machine the

Fig. 24 **Injector piston, made from 1/2" C.R.S. round rod**

43

piston can be clamped in a V-block and the flats cut with a milling cutter.

After the flats have been milled or filed, clamp the piston in the V-block, then locate, drill and ream the .251 hole. Chuck the piston in the lathe using a 3-jaw chuck and turn the 45 degree tapered end 1/16" back. The tapered end is important because it will help the piston enter the injection cylinder smoothly.

Assemble the injection lever, links and piston as shown in

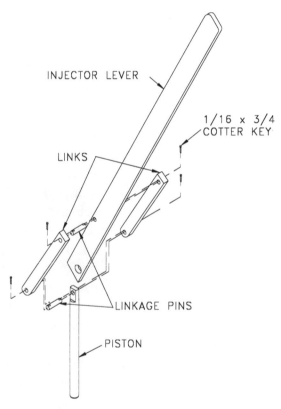

Fig. 25   **The injection linkage assembly**

figure 25. Use 1/16" x 3/4" cotter keys to hold the link and piston pins in place.

Weld the right side base from **figure 8** and the right side top brace from **figure 13** to the frame. Use C-clamps to hold them in position while welding. See **figure 26**.

Fig. 26 Welding the right side base and the right side top brace to the frame.

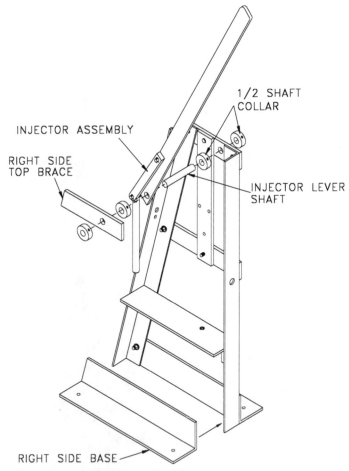

Fig. 27 Assembling the linkage assembly to the frame.

The injector assembly mounts to the frame as shown in **figure 27**. The four 1/2" inside diameter shaft collars shown in the drawing can be made or you can buy them at most hardware and farm supply stores.

THE ADJUSTABLE WORK TABLE

The purpose of the adjustable table is to raise the mold up forcing the mold sprue tight against the injection nozzle. It's a unique feature of the machine and with it molds of varying sizes can be used on the machine.

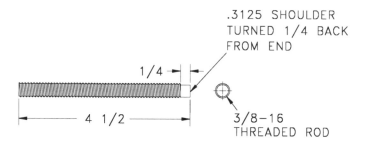

Fig. 28   **Screw shaft for the adjustable table.**

The 4-1/2" long threaded rod section for the table assembly is shown in **figure 28**. Using the lathe, mount the threaded rod in a 3-jaw chuck and turn the .3125 shoulder 1/4" back. Be careful not to damage the threads.

The table is made from a piece of 1/4" x 3" x 4" C.R.S. flat bar and is shown in **figure 29**. Center the table in a 4-jaw chuck. Center drill, then drill through 5/16". Counter bore to 3/4" diameter, .050" deep. Remove and rechuck to counter bore the other side to 3/4" diameter, .050 deep. I used the lathe to drill and bore the center hole in the adjustable table, but a drill press could be used as well.

The assembly sequence for the adjustable table is shown in **figure 30**. Begin by placing a 1/4" flat washer on the shouldered end of the threaded rod. Set the 5/16" hole in the table on to the

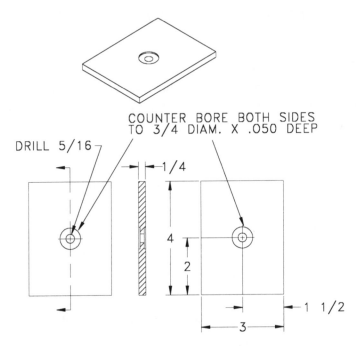

Fig. 29 **Adjustable work table, made from 1/4" x 3" x 4" C.R.S. flat bar**

shouldered end of the threaded rod so that the 1/4" flat washer rests inside the counter bore on the underside of the table. Place another 1/4" flat washer on the shouldered end of the threaded rod protruding through the top side of the table. The washer should rest inside the counter bore and flush with the table surface. Braze the top side washer to the threaded rod. Take care not to braze the washer or threaded rod to the table. When complete, the threaded rod should turn freely inside the table while the table remains stationary.

Thread the completed assembly into the 3/8-16 hole located in the stationary work base as shown in **figure 30.**

48

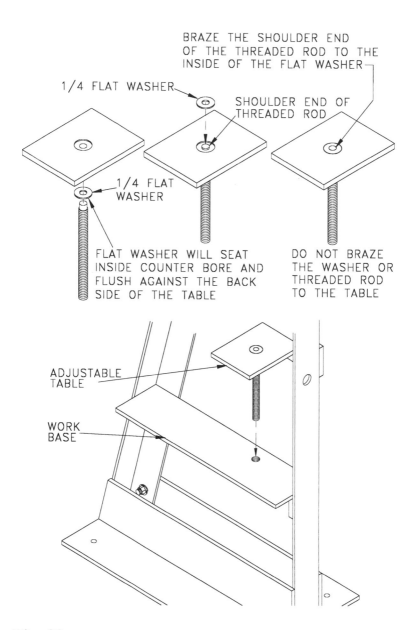

BRAZE THE SHOULDER END
OF THE THREADED ROD TO THE
INSIDE OF THE FLAT WASHER

1/4 FLAT WASHER

SHOULDER END OF
THREADED ROD

1/4 FLAT
WASHER

FLAT WASHER WILL SEAT
INSIDE COUNTER BORE AND
FLUSH AGAINST THE BACK
SIDE OF THE TABLE

DO NOT BRAZE
THE WASHER OR
THREADED ROD
TO THE TABLE

ADJUSTABLE
TABLE

WORK
BASE

Fig. 30

49

THE HEATER BLOCK ASSEMBLY

A drawing of the heater block is shown in **figure 32**. The term, *step drilling* will be used to describe the drilling operations involved in making the heater block. Step drilling means starting with a small drill bit most likely 1/8" and then changing to progressively larger drill sizes to form the finished hole or bore. Step drilling preserves the proper center location of the hole. It's much better to change drill bits a few times than to try and drill a hole all at once and ruin the part.

Begin making the heater block by cutting a piece of 1" x 1-1/2" C.R.S. bar stock to a length slightly longer than 4". Center the block in a 4-jaw chuck to face off the end. Reposition in the

Fig. 31 Reaming the injection cylinder.

chuck to face off the other end. Finished length to be 4".

Remove the heater block from the chuck to layout the location for the .501 cylinder bore and the .374 bore for the heater cartridge. Reposition the heater block in the 4-jaw chuck and step drill the cylinder bore to 31/64" diameter. Then ream through with a .501 chucking reamer. Set the compound rest on the lathe and turn a 45-degree chamfer edge on the cylinder bore 1/16" deep.

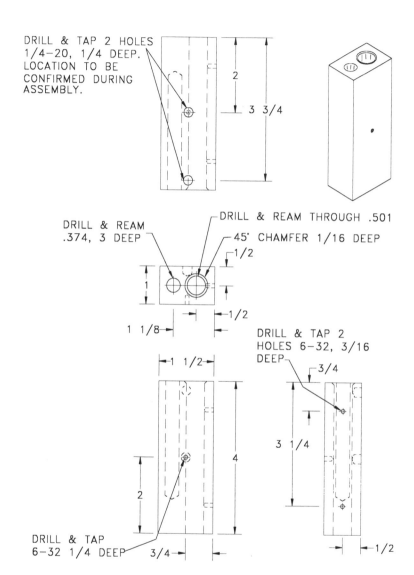

Fig. 32 Heater block, made from 1" x 1-1/2" C.R.S. bar stock

51

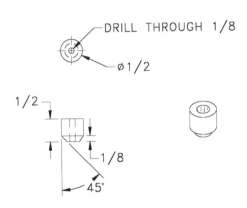

Fig. 33

Injection nozzle, made from 1/2" C.R.S. round rod

Reposition the heater block in the 4-jaw chuck. Center drill then step drill the bore for the cartridge heater to 23/64", 3" deep. Then ream the bore with a .374" chucking reamer.

Remove the heater block from the 4-jaw chuck and locate, drill and tap the 6-32 hole, 3/16" deep centered in the front of the block. Be sure and set the drill stop on the drill press to prevent the hole from being drilled through the cylinder wall. This hole will be used to attach the thermometer.

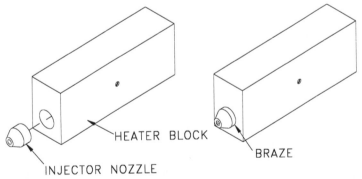

Fig. 34

Locate, drill and tap the two 6-32 holes 3/16" deep on the right side of the heater block. Again, be careful not to drill these holes through the cylinder wall. They will be used to attach the thermostat.

Locations are given for two 1/4-20 holes 1/4" deep in the back of the heater block, but it is best to locate these holes during construction and I will show you how that is done later in the sequence.

The injection nozzle is shown in **figure 33**. Make it by chucking a 1" length of 1/2" C.R.S. round rod in a 3-jaw chuck so that 5/8" extends out past the chuck. Face off the end. Center drill, then drill 1/8", 5/8" deep. Adjust the compound rest to

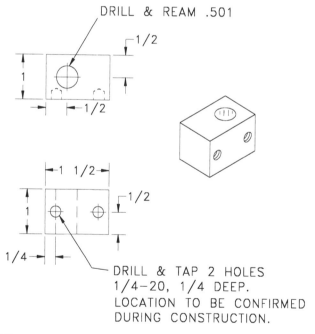

Fig. 35 **Piston alignment bushing, made from 1" x 1-1/2" C.R.S. bar stock.**

turn the 45-degree taper end 1/8" back. Measure back 1/2" from the end and part off.

Insert the injection nozzle into the .501 cylinder hole located on the bottom of the heater block as shown in **figure 34**. The tapered end of the nozzle will extend 1/4" outside the heater block leaving 1/4" inside the cylinder. Braze the nozzle in place using care not to braze over the surface of the tapered end.

Cut a length of 1" x 1-1/2" C.R.S. bar stock slightly longer than 1" for the alignment bushing shown in **figure 35**. Center in a 4-jaw chuck and face off the end. Reposition in the chuck to face off the other end. Finished length to be 1". Remove from the chuck and carefully layout the location of the .501 bore. Reposition the alignment bushing in the 4-jaw chuck. Center drill, then step drill through to 31/64" diameter. Ream with a .501 chucking reamer. Locations for the two holes tapped 1/4-20, 1/4" deep are shown in the drawing, but it is best to locate these holes later during construction.

MOUNTING THE HEATER BLOCK & GUIDE BUSHING TO THE HEATER POST

The heater block and guide bushing must be aligned properly on the heater post for the injector piston to travel smoothly through both without binding. Before they can be permanently mounted you will need to locate the 1/4-20 mounting holes in each one. The following method to accomplish this worked well for me.

First, measure 2-7/8" up from the bottom of the heater post and scribe a line. Measure up from the bottom of the heater post 5-3/8" and scribe another line. See **figure 37.**

You will need two, 2" hose clamps to temporarily hold the heater block and guide bushing in position. Prepare the hose clamps by unscrewing them all the way to separate the ends. Place them around the heater post and screw the ends back together. See **figure 36.**

Place the heater block flush

Fig. 36 Photo showing the hose clamps on heater post.

against the heater post aligning the top edge of the block with the scribed line located 2-7/8" from the bottom of the post. The 1/2" injection cylinder will be on your right as you face the front of the heater block. Hold the block in position with one hand and drop a hose clamp down over it. Tighten the hose clamp until it holds the heater

SCRIBE LINES FOR POSITIONING HEATER BLOCK AND GUIDE BUSHING

HEATER POST

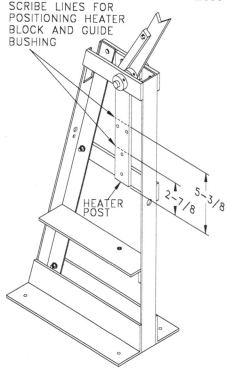

Fig. 37

55

block securely against the heater post. The edges of both sides of the block should be aligned with the edges of the heater post and the top edge of the heater block should be aligned with the scribed line. If not, loosen the clamp to adjust the block to its proper position.

Slide the guide bushing on to the injector piston. Locate the bushing flush against the heater post with its top edge aligned with the scribed line located 5-3/8" from the bottom of the heater post. While holding the bushing in place with one hand tighten the other hose clamp until it holds the bushing securely against the heater post. The edges of both sides of the bushing should be aligned with the edges of the heater post and the top edge of the bushing should be aligned with the scribe line.

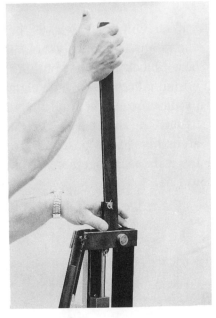

Fig. 38 **If the linkage binds, push down on it with your thumb as shown in the photo.**

The final step is to align the heater block and guide bushing with the injector piston. To accomplish this, loosen the hose clamps slightly. Pull the injector lever down slowly while guiding the injector piston into the cylinder of the heater block. The linkage may bind, but you should be able to free the bind by pushing against the linkage with your thumb while pulling

56

down the injector lever. See **figure 38**. Continue pulling the lever until the injector piston is stopped by the bottom of the heater block. With the piston still against the bottom of the heater block, retighten the hose clamps. Operate the lever a few times to make sure the piston still travels freely.

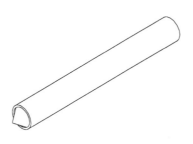

Fig. 38 Transfer punch

Now is a good time to locate the 1/4-20 mounting holes in the heater block and guide bushing. This can be done with a transfer punch. A transfer punch is a punch that has been sized to fit a template hole, in this case the 1/4" holes in the heater post. It has a small hardened tip on its end and works by inserting it in each of the 1/4" holes in the heater post. The end of the punch is tapped with a hammer. This makes a prick mark on the heater block and guide bushing referenced with the holes in the heater post. Transfer punches can be

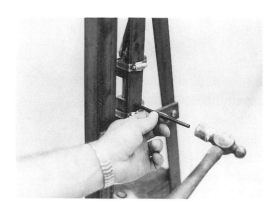

Fig. 39 locating the hole locations in the heater block and guide bushing using a transfer punch.

57

purchased at a reasonable cost or you can make your own. If you make your own you will need a 6" length of 1/4" drill rod. We use drill rod because the tip must be hardened. Center the drill rod in the lathe chuck. Turn a small point on its end. Remove the drill rod from the lathe. Heat the end or your newly formed transfer punch to bright red and then immediately quench it in water. Temper the end by reheating it to a straw color and then quench it in water. **Figure 38** shows a drawing of the end of a transfer punch. The photo in **figure 39** shows using the transfer punch to locate the holes in the heater block.

Now that the hole locations have been marked, remove the heater block and guide bushing from heater post. Drill and tap the holes 1/4-20, 1/4" deep in each of the marked locations. Remember to set the depth stop on the drill press so you don't drill too deep and enter the cylinder wall.

INSTALLING THE THERMOMETER

An oven thermometer mounted to the front surface of the heater block works well for tracking the temperature of the heater block during operation of the machine. Oven thermometers are manufactured under several different brand names. Not all have the same temperature range. Some will have a range of from 100 to 400 degrees, 100 to 475 degrees, 100-575 degrees and

Fig. 40   **Thermometer**

100-600 degrees. Oven thermometers can be found at grocery stores, hardware stores, K-mart, Wal-Mart etc. Look in the kitchen utensil's isle. Prices range from $2.99 - $5.99. For our purpose it is best to use a thermometer with a temperature range of at least 500 degrees. All of the

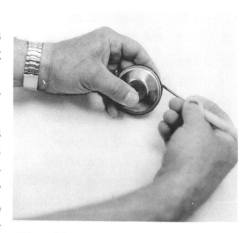

Fig. 41 **Prying the thermometer apart**

Fig. 42 The thermometer as it looks when it is disassembled. Notice that the stand has been trimmed from the bezel.

oven thermometers I have seen have been easy to disassemble by prying the back case off with a small screw driver. Kind of like removing the back of a watch. Once inside the case you will see a small heat sensitive spring mounted to the backside of the dial plate. The spring is connected to the dial needle. When the heat sensitive spring feels heat it begins to expand and the dial needle

59

moves to a higher temperature. As the spring cools it begins to shrink causing the needle to move to a lower temperature.

Oven thermometer bezels will have a metal stand which enables them to be set on an oven shelf. The stand gets in our way so cut it off with a pair of tin snips. Remove the sharp edge left by the tin snips with a file and/or piece of sand paper.

With the thermometer disassembled, drill an 1/8" hole in the center of the base. Fasten the base to the heater block with a 6-32 x 1/4" machine screw as shown in **figure 45**. Once the base is fastened in position, snap the front bezel assembly back in place.

INSTALLING THE CARTRIDGE HEATER

A cartridge heater is a stainless steel tube with a heat coil sealed inside. A photo of one is shown in **figure 43**. They come in many different sizes and are used in many different applications. The cartridge heater used in this application is rated at 250 watts. It measures 3/8" diameter and is 3" long. It's manufactured by Chromalox® and is listed under part #CRP-203A025. I have seen them in the Grainger® catalog and some

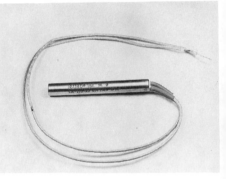

Fig. 43 **The cartridge heater**

appliance parts stores may have them. I know this is going to be a tough to find item so I bought an extra quantity of them. They are available to those of you wanting to build the machine.

Refer to the sources section at the back of the book for price information and answers to your questions on how to place an order.

Installing the heater cartridge is simply a matter of inserting it into the .374" bored hole located in the heater block. See **figure 45**. It will be a fairly snug fit, but will still be loose enough to allow for heat expansion.

Safety factors concerning cartridge heaters:

1. Electric cartridge heaters should not be bent or deformed because heater insulation can be damaged, leading to electrical problems and a shorter heater life.

2. Since electric heaters develop high temperatures, extreme care should be taken to:

a. Not use heaters in an environment containing combustible liquids, gases or vapors.

b. Keep combustible materials far enough away to be free of the effects of high temperatures.

3. Cartridge heaters should be provided with snug fitting holes, but at the same time the hole must be large enough to allow for heater expansion.

INSTALLING THE THERMOSTAT

The thermostat is manufactured by the Chromalox® corporation. Its listed part number is SA-701. This type of thermostat is called a low wattage (appliance) thermostat. It is used in a variety of applications and is designed for those appliances that permit direct contact with a heated surface. One example would be an electric iron.

The adjustable contact thermostat used in this project will be even harder to find at the retail level than the cartridge heater so we thought it best to stock a quantity of these as well. Those of you wishing to purchase this item can refer to the sources section at the back of the book for further information.

A drawing of the thermostat is shown in **figure 44**. As you can see by its size it's perfect for this application. The temperature range of the thermostat is 250-600 degrees with a temperature differential from 5-20 degrees.

It works by means of a set of heat sensitive bimetal points contained inside the thermostat housing. The bimetal points react to the surface temperature of the heater block.

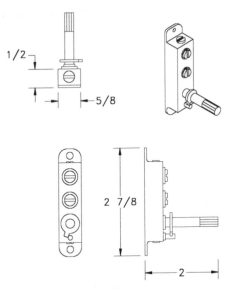

Fig. 44 250-600 degree adjustable thermostat

When the points close, they complete the circuit and power is supplied to the cartridge heater causing it to heat the heater block. When the points open power is no longer being supplied to the cartridge heater and the block begins to cool. The adjustable knob on the thermostat controls the point gap and thus the temperature range. Turning the knob counter clockwise increases the point gap decreasing the temperature of the heater block. Turning the knob clockwise decreases the point gap and increases the temperature of the heater block. Now that we understand how it works lets mount the thermostat to the side of

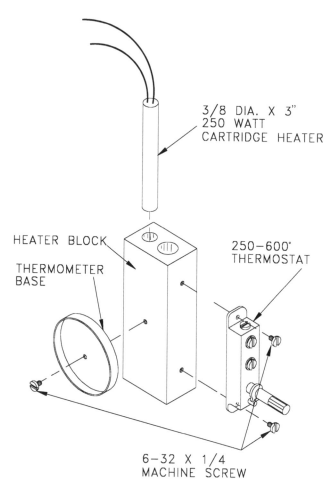

3/8 DIA. X 3"
250 WATT
CARTRIDGE HEATER

HEATER BLOCK

THERMOMETER
BASE

250-600°
THERMOSTAT

6-32 X 1/4
MACHINE SCREW

Fig. 45

the heater block with two, 6-32 x 1/4 machine screws as shown in **figure 45**.

Bolt the alignment bushing and heater block to the heater post as shown in **figure 46**. Note that the bottom bolt used is a

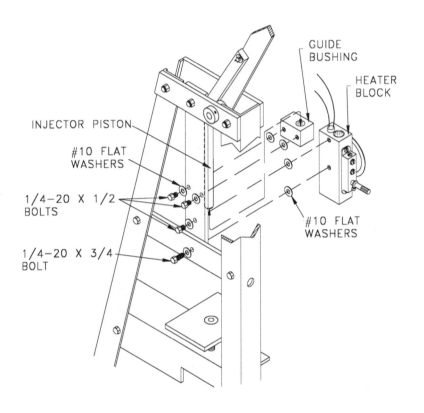

Fig. 46

1/4-20 x 3/4" and the other three bolts are 1/4-20 x 1/2". The extra length of the bottom bolt is needed because it must pass through both the cross brace and the heater post. The #10 flat washers between the heater block and the heater post are for spacers. They create an air gap that reduces the rate of heat transfer from the heater block to the heater post.

The shaft on the thermostat is not long enough to extend out past the frame so we need to make the shaft extension shown in **figure 47**. Make it from a 1-3/4" length of 3/8" C.R.S. round rod. Place the shaft blank in a 3-jaw chuck. Center drill and then drill 15/64", 1/2" deep. Then ream the 15/64" hole with a .251 chucking reamer.

Turn the blank around in the chuck to machine the opposite end. Turn the 1/4" shoulder 1/2" back from the end. Remove the thermostat extension from the 3-jaw chuck and clamp it in a V-block. Drill and tap the 6-32 hole for the set screw through to the .251 hole.

A 5 amp, 120 volt toggle switch is used to turn the machine

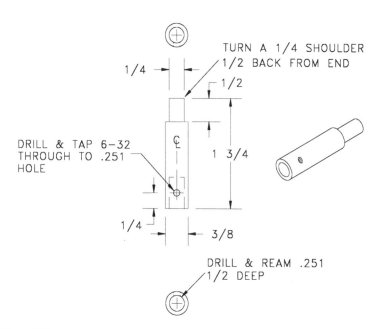

Fig. 47 **Thermostat extension, made from 3/8" C.R.S. round rod**

Fig. 48
Indicator light & on/off switch

off and on. These can be purchased at electronics, hardware and auto parts stores.

The indicator light will show when the machine is cycling on and off. The light is referred to as a 120-volt red neon indicator lamp. It can be purchased at Radio Shack and its part number is 272-712. Similar lights can be purchased at

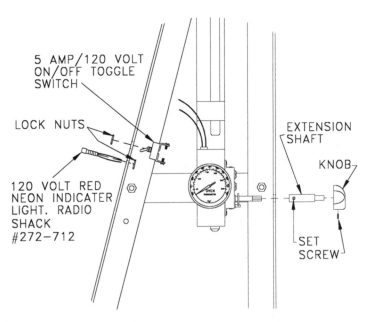

5 AMP/120 VOLT
ON/OFF TOGGLE
SWITCH

LOCK NUTS

120 VOLT RED
NEON INDICATER
LIGHT. RADIO
SHACK
#272-712

EXTENSION
SHAFT

KNOB

SET
SCREW

Fig. 49

hardware stores and auto parts stores. Just make sure they are rated for 120 volts.

A drawing showing the installation of the thermostat extension, the knob for the thermostat, the on/off switch and the indicator light is shown in **figure 49**. Chances are that the knob mentioned will come with the thermostat. If not, a knob can be purchased at hardware or electronic stores. It will be listed as an appliance knob. It should be of a size to fit the 1/4" thermostat shaft and have a set screw for securing it to the shaft.

WIRING THE MACHINE

Before wiring the machine, holes need to be drilled in the frame for routing the wires. Put a piece of masking tape over the cylinder hole in the heater block to prevent metal chips from falling into the cylinder. Drill four, 5/16" holes in the frame at the approximate locations shown in **figure 50**. Chamfer both ends of each hole with a 1/2" counter sink drill to remove any sharp edges that could cut the insulation on the wires.

About 2 feet of high temperature wire will be needed to wire the machine. The wire on the cartridge heater is high temperature wire able to withstand the temperatures of the machine. It is important that the rest of the wire you use be a high temperature wire as well. If you don't use high temperature wire it's certain that the insulation on normal wire would melt and cause a dangerous short in the circuit. The proper wire to use is either 14 or 16 gauge appliance wire with a temperature rating of at least 450 degrees centigrade (852 degrees Fahrenheit). Appliance wire is stranded, nickel coated copper and will have a mica glass insulation. High temperature appliance wire rated at 450 degrees centigrade can be purchased

DRILL 4, 5/16 HOLES THROUGH
THE FRAME IN THE APPROXIMATE
LOCATIONS SHOWN. CHAMFER
BOTH ENDS OF EACH HOLE WITH
A 1/2" COUNTER SINK DRILL TO
REMOVE SHARP EDGES THAT COULD
CUT THE INSULATION ON WIRES.

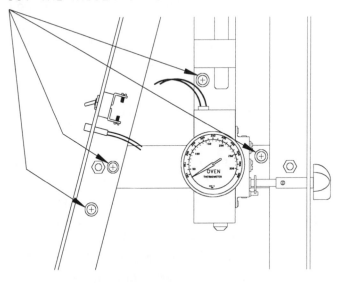

Fig. 50   **Drilling holes in the frame for wiring.**

at most appliance parts stores. You can expect to pay $1.50 or more per foot for it and as mentioned earlier you will need about 2' of it. You may also be able to find this type of wire at an appliance junk yard because it is often used in electric dryers near the heating element. It may also be found in some electric ovens.

A 6' long, 120 volt power cord with a ground and at least 18 gauge wire is used on the machine. For safety reasons, it is very important that the machine be grounded.

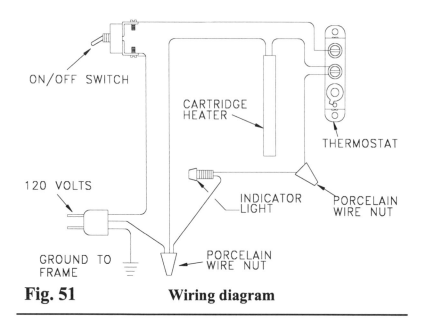

ON/OFF SWITCH

CARTRIDGE
HEATER

THERMOSTAT

120 VOLTS

INDICATOR
LIGHT

PORCELAIN
WIRE NUT

GROUND TO
FRAME

PORCELAIN
WIRE NUT

Fig. 51   **Wiring diagram**

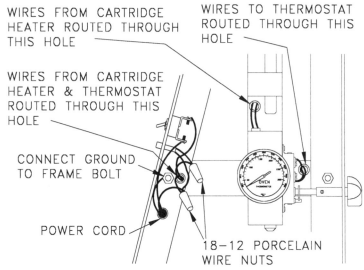

WIRES FROM CARTRIDGE
HEATER ROUTED THROUGH
THIS HOLE

WIRES TO THERMOSTAT
ROUTED THROUGH THIS
HOLE

WIRES FROM CARTRIDGE
HEATER & THERMOSTAT
ROUTED THROUGH THIS
HOLE

CONNECT GROUND
TO FRAME BOLT

POWER CORD

18-12 PORCELAIN
WIRE NUTS

Fig. 52

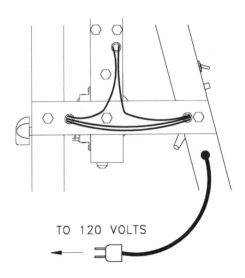

TO 120 VOLTS

Fig. 53

The wiring diagram for the machine is shown in **figure 51.** The drawings in **figures 52 and 53** show how the wires are routed. It is very important to make and install covers for the exposed wires and terminal connections. There are four covers to make and the next few drawings will show how to make them. All of the covers can be made from 20 to 24 gauge hot roll steel. Aluminum works fine too. Mine were made from an aluminum kick plate that came from a discarded storm door. The bends to form the covers

Fig 54 Sheet metal tool

70

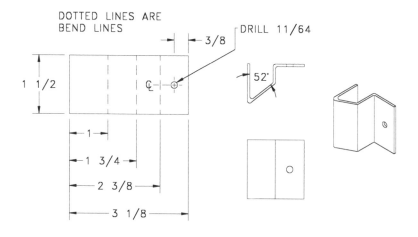

DOTTED LINES ARE
BEND LINES

DRILL 11/64

3/8

1 1/2

Ȼ

52°

1

1 3/4

2 3/8

3 1/8

Fig. 55   **Cover for the cartridge heater wires**

can be made with a Vise- Grip® sheet metal tool. The photo in **figure 54** shows the tool.

Make the cover for cartridge heater wires following the layout drawing in **figure 55**. The dotted lines in the drawing represent the bend lines. Cut the piece out, drill the 11/64" hole and bend it to the shape shown. Before mounting the cover, place a piece of masking tape over the cylinder hole to prevent metal chips from falling in. Raise or remove the injector piston. Use the drilled hole in the cover tab as a guide to locate and drill an 11/64" hole through the heater post. Mount the cover to the heater post with an 8-32 x 1/2 machine screw with nut. **Figure 60** shows the cover installed.

The thermostat cover is shown in the layout drawing in **figure 56**. The dotted lines represent bend lines. Cut the form

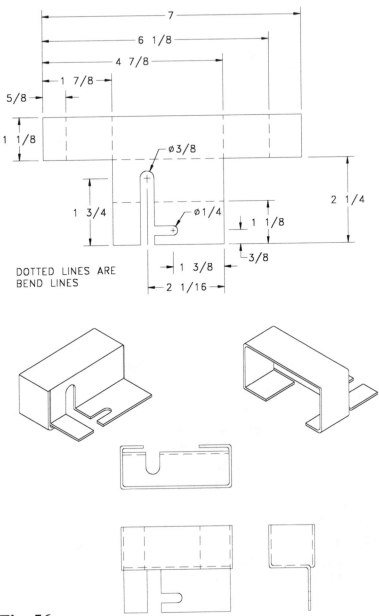

Fig. 56

Thermostat cover

out and bend it to the shape shown in the perspective drawings. Before mounting the thermostat cover, remove the nut from the bolt located just to the right of the thermostat. It's the one that holds the center cross brace to the frame. Slide the cover into position around the thermostat. The 3/8" slot in the cover will fit over the thermostat shaft. The 1/4" slotted hole fits over the 1/4" bolt used for fastening the center cross brace to the frame. To prevent a short, make sure that the electrical terminals on

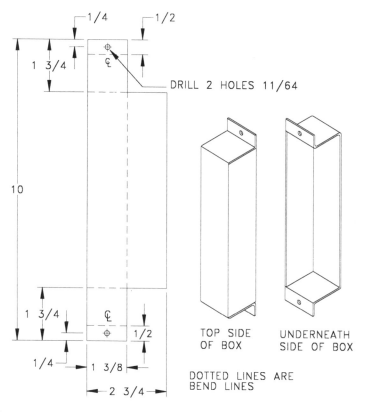

Fig. 57 **Cover box for the on/off switch, the indicator light and wiring.**

the thermostat are not touching the cover and there is plenty of clearance between the two to prevent it from happening. When the cover is positioned properly, replace the nut on the frame bolt and tighten it.

Layout the box used to cover the wiring, the exposed terminals of the on/off switch and indicator light as shown in **figure 57**. The dotted lines will represent bend lines. Cut the form out, drill the 11/64" holes and bend to the shape shown in

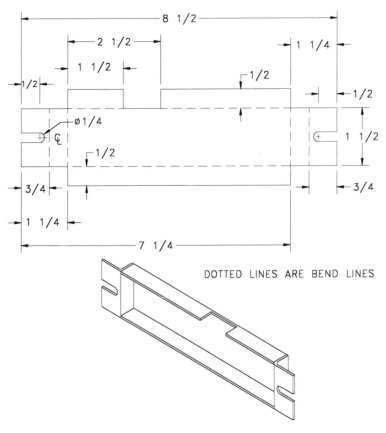

DOTTED LINES ARE BEND LINES

Fig. 58   **Left side wire cover**

the perspective view.

Locate the mounting holes for the switch cover by holding it against the inside of the front post in the approximate location shown in **figure 60**. Be sure that there is plenty of clearance between the terminals, the on/off switch and the cover. Hold the

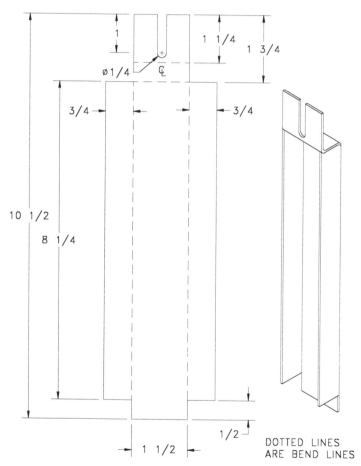

Fig. 59   **Left side wire cover**

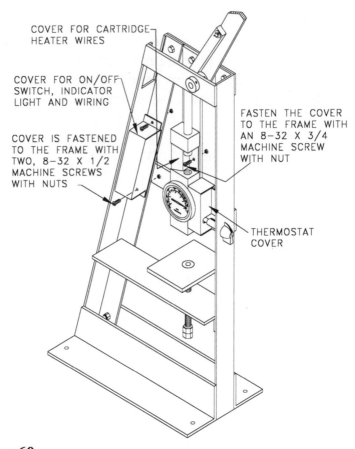

COVER FOR CARTRIDGE
HEATER WIRES

COVER FOR ON/OFF
SWITCH, INDICATOR
LIGHT AND WIRING

COVER IS FASTENED
TO THE FRAME WITH
TWO, 8-32 X 1/2
MACHINE SCREWS
WITH NUTS

FASTEN THE COVER
TO THE FRAME WITH
AN 8-32 X 3/4
MACHINE SCREW
WITH NUT

THERMOSTAT
COVER

Fig. 60

cover in position with one hand. Then drill 11/64" holes through the frame to match the 11/64" hole in each tab end of the cover.

Layout the left side wire covers on a sheet of 20 gauge sheet metal as shown in **figure 58 & 59**. Cut out the form for each cover and make the bends as shown in the perspective drawings. Mount them to the left side frame using the existing frame bolts as shown in **figure 62 and 63**.

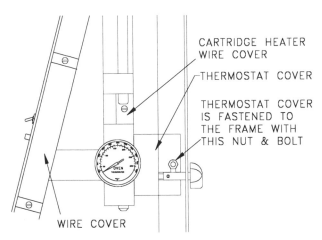

CARTRIDGE HEATER
WIRE COVER

THERMOSTAT COVER

THERMOSTAT COVER
IS FASTENED TO
THE FRAME WITH
THIS NUT & BOLT

WIRE COVER

Fig. 61   Right side wire and terminal covers

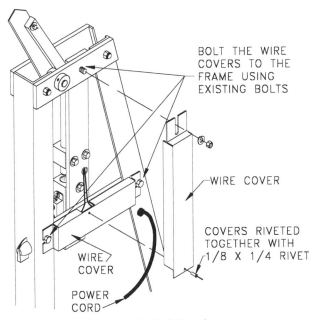

BOLT THE WIRE
COVERS TO THE
FRAME USING
EXISTING BOLTS

WIRE COVER

COVERS RIVETED
TOGETHER WITH
1/8 X 1/4 RIVET

WIRE
COVER

POWER
CORD

Fig. 62   Mounting the left side wire covers

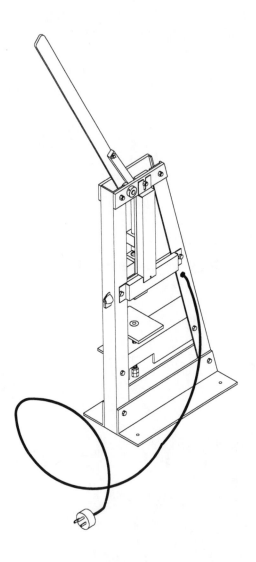

Fig. 63

Congratulations, your injection molding machine is complete and ready to go to work. But first you need a mold. The next section will show you how to make a simple mold so you can test your machine.

INJECTION MOLDS

To convert the softened thermoplastic produced by the injection molding machine into a useful item requires a mold. The mold will contain a cavity that matches the desired shape of the item to be produced. The purpose of the mold is to confine the plastic material while it hardens to the desired shape.

Once the plastic hardens, you must be able to remove the newly formed item from the mold. For this reason all injection molds will have at least two sections and more complicated molds can require more sections. The point at which the mold sections come together is called the *parting line*. It is common practice to place a 2 degree slope on mold surfaces that are perpendicular to the parting line. This is called the *draft* and its purpose is to make parts easier to remove from the mold. You will find that the draft is not always necessary, but at the very least surfaces must be perpendicular to the parting line. As you

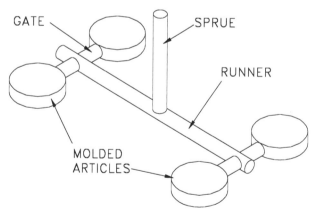

Fig. 64

gain experience making molds you will learn when draft is necessary and when it is not.

Of course the plastic must be able to enter the sealed mold cavity. This entrance to the mold is called the *sprue*. In the molds we will be making for our projects the sprue opening will be located along the parting line. When a single item is being made in the mold the sprue will feed directly into the mold cavity. When multiple parts are made in a single mold the sprue will feed into a *runner*. A runner can be described as a main highway. Along the highway there are side roads or arteries that branch off to feed the mold cavities. These branches are called *gates*. See **figure 64**.

MOLD CONSTRUCTION

Before a mold can be made, you must develop a good mental picture of what it is you want to produce. Keep in mind that what you want to produce is limited only by your imagination. The size however will be limited by the capacity of your machine. Once a mental picture is formed, it is brought to life by placing it on paper in the form of a rough sketch. The rough sketch is transformed into a working drawing with dimensions. The working drawing is used to create the layout of the mold.

Molds are usually machined from cold roll steel. It is fairly inexpensive and wears well. The only draw back to using steel molds is their tendency to rust during storage. Molds can also be machined from aluminum which doesn't rust and in my opinion is much easier to machine than steel. But because aluminum is a soft metal, molds made from it can be easily damaged. Also, the sprue opening may experience more wear on an aluminum mold.

Mold making always requires a certain amount of machine and hand work. It's nice to have a power hacksaw or bandsaw for cutting bar stock to a desired size, but a hand hacksaw will do the job. It just takes longer. A set of drill bits from 1/8" to 1/2" are needed as well as a good quality tap and die set with sizes 1/4" through 1/2". A fine, medium and coarse set of hand files will come in handy too. And I usually keep a couple of sheets each of 300 and 600 grit wet/dry sand paper around for polishing the inside mold surfaces. At the very least you should have a drill press and with it you can make the first mold in the project. A lathe is really the most important mold making tool and without it you will be limited as to what you can produce. Other more exotic equipment can be found in a commercial shop. Things such as a milling machine with attachments, a surface grinder, metal shaper, grinding machines, and on and on. But you won't need all the equipment found in a commercial shop. As you proceed with the hobby I think you will discover that most of your work can be accomplished on the lathe.

When you design your molds, keep in mind that more complicated mold designs can require the use of more specialized equipment. In the small home shop time is not as important as it is in the commercial shop and we can work at our leisure designing molds around available equipment. And usually we can come up with alternate methods for doing complicated jobs. For example, in a mold shop, lettering, engraving and delicate detail work are often done with a pantograph or duplicating machine. With a little practice we can learn to do the same high quality detail work and lettering with a hand grinder or Dremel® tool.

Another method of making molds is by casting. This method is used when an existing part is to be duplicated. Casting is also a good way of creating molds for complicated parts or those parts with intricate detail. For instance, a pattern can be machined out of metal or carved out of wood, plastic or other material and then the mold can be cast rather than machined. Later we will learn more about making a mold by casting when we duplicate an appliance knob using molding plaster of paris as the casting medium. We will also learn how aluminum filled epoxy can be used to cast molds.

There are other methods of making molds such as hobbing, electrical erosion, chemical erosion and others, but these are beyond the scope of this book and of the average home shop.

MAKING THE FIRST MOLD

We will begin by making a simple mold. The purpose of the mold will be to form two 1/2" diameter plastic pieces 1/2" long. For the lack of a better term I am going to call this mold a slug mold and the plastic pieces it produces will be referred to as slugs. With this mold you will become familiar with operating the injection molding machine. You will also learn how plastic reacts when it is heated and what happens after it is injected in the mold. Besides being a good mold to learn the

Fig. 65   **Slug Mold**

process on it will be handy for converting plastic strips to 1/2" diameter cylindrical shapes which will be easier to load in the machine. And if you have just shot a mold and you have plastic left in the injection cylinder you can shoot it into the slug mold. Eventually you can convert a lot of plastic strips to easier to store and more usable plastic slugs.

Ø1/2

THIS ANGLE WILL
WILL END UP BEING
THE SAME AS THE
ANGLE ON THE END
OF YOUR DRILL BIT

1/2

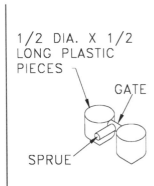

1/2 DIA. X 1/2
LONG PLASTIC
PIECES

GATE

SPRUE

We will need a mold to make
2 plastic pieces as shown.

This is how the plastic
pieces will look when
they come out of the
mold.

Fig. 66

Figure 66 contains a drawing of one of the plastic slugs we will be making with the slug mold. The drawing next to it shows how they will look after coming out of the mold.

Figure 67 shows the layout for the bottom half of the mold. Make it from a 3/4" length of 1 x 2" C.R.S. bar stock. Mating surfaces of the mold must be faced off in the lathe or filed flat. This is done to prevent plastic from squeezing out at the parting line.

Locate and step drill the two 1/2" diameter holes 1/2" deep. Cut the 1/8" wide x 1/16" deep gate using a small round file.

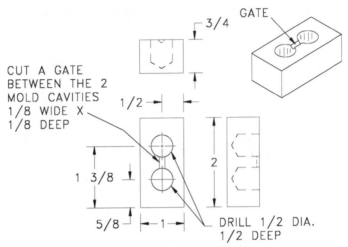

Fig. 67   Bottom half of mold made from a 3/4" length of 1" x 2" C.R.S. bar stock.

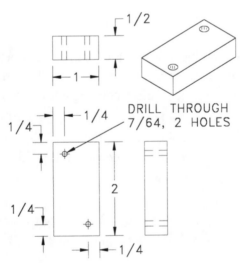

Fig. 68 Top half of mold made from a 1/2" length of 1" x 2" C.R.S. bar stock.

84

The top mold blank is shown in **figure 68**. Make it from a 1/2" length of 1" x 2" C.R.S. bar stock. Drill two 7/64" holes through the mold half for guide pins in the locations shown. The purpose of the guide pins is to ensure that the mold halves will always be assembled in exactly the same way every time.

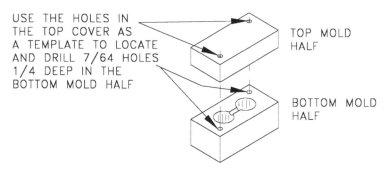

USE THE HOLES IN THE TOP COVER AS A TEMPLATE TO LOCATE AND DRILL 7/64 HOLES 1/4 DEEP IN THE BOTTOM MOLD HALF

TOP MOLD HALF

BOTTOM MOLD HALF

Fig. 69

Put the two mold halves together. All sides of the mold halves must be perfectly aligned. The next step will be to drill 7/64" holes 1/4" deep in the bottom mold half using the existing 7/64" holes in the top mold half for guides. See **figure 69**. To accomplish this, place the mold halves in a drill vise making sure they remain together and aligned. Set the drill stop for the depth necessary. Align the drill with a 7/64" hole in the top mold half. Using a 7/64" bit, drill 1/4" into the bottom mold half. Repeat the above steps to drill the other 7/64" hole 1/4" into the bottom mold half. Separate the mold. Secure the top half of the mold in the vise and ream the 7/64" holes with a .126" chucking reamer. Next, place the bottom mold half in the drill vise and ream the 7/64" holes with a .124" chucking reamer.

Make each guide pin from a 1/2" length of 1/8" C.R.S.

round rod. See **figure 70**.
Grind a small 1/64" chamfer
on each end of each pin.
Press the guide pins into the
.124 holes in the bottom
mold half.

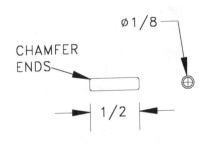

Put the two mold halves
back together and mark the
location for the sprue hole
with a center punch. It will

**Fig. 70   Guide pin, made
from 1/8" C.R.S. round rod**

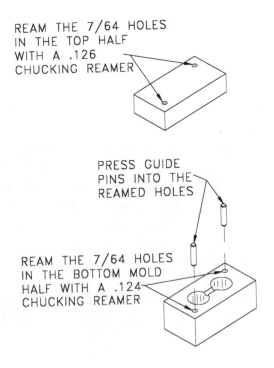

Fig. 71

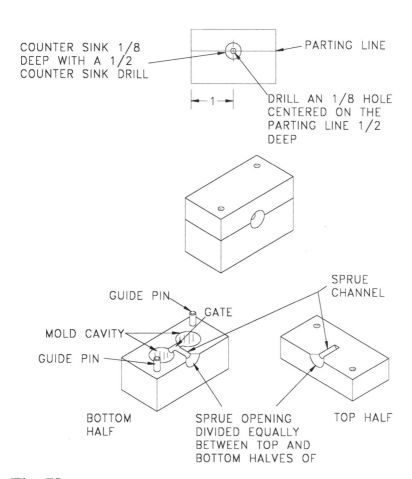

COUNTER SINK 1/8
DEEP WITH A 1/2
COUNTER SINK DRILL

PARTING LINE

|← 1 →|

DRILL AN 1/8 HOLE
CENTERED ON THE
PARTING LINE 1/2
DEEP

SPRUE
CHANNEL

GUIDE PIN

GATE

MOLD CAVITY

GUIDE PIN

BOTTOM
HALF

SPRUE OPENING
DIVIDED EQUALLY
BETWEEN TOP AND
BOTTOM HALVES OF

TOP HALF

Fig. 72

be centered on the parting line as shown in **figure 72**. Clamp the
assembled mold in the drill vise. Set the drill stop to drill 1/2"
deep. Using a 1/8" bit, drill the sprue hole through to the gate.
Counter sink the sprue opening 1/8" deep using a 1/2", 45
degree countersink drill.

87

Congratulations, you have just successfully completed making your first injection mold. Now that we have a mold we can try out the new injection molding machine, but first a few words about safety.

SAFETY FIRST

Before operating your new injection molding machine for the first time, check all wiring to see that it has been done correctly. All exposed wires and terminals must be covered. The machine should only be plugged into a GFI outlet. GFI stands for ground fault interrupter. GFI outlets have a circuit breaker as part of the outlet. An electrical short or other problem in the wiring of your machine will flip the circuit breaker off and cut the power to the machine.

During operation the heater block gets very hot reaching temperatures in excess of 400 degrees. Heat from the block radiates to parts of the frame. **Figure 73** shows the area of the machine that poses the greatest burn danger. If you touch a hot surface on the machine it can cause a severe burn. The softened plastic produced by the machine can burn too. And it's like wax, it sticks to your skin and keeps burning.

The plastic injection molding machine is an appliance much like your kitchen oven or the iron you use to press your clothes. The only difference being, that instead of baking cookies, frying hamburgers or pressing your clothes you are melting plastic. Common sense will tell you that if you're not careful taking the cookies out of the oven you can burn yourself. And we all should have learned at an early age that it is not a good idea to touch the surface of a hot iron. Wear leather gloves when feeding plastic in the machine. It's easy to accidentally brush

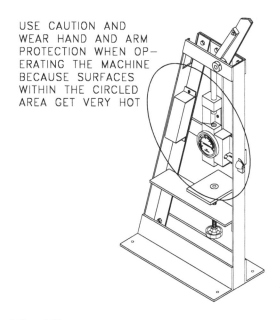

USE CAUTION AND WEAR HAND AND ARM PROTECTION WHEN OP-ERATING THE MACHINE BECAUSE SURFACES WITHIN THE CIRCLED AREA GET VERY HOT

Fig. 73

your arm against the hot surfaces of the machine so it's a good idea to wear a long sleeve shirt. It's best that the shirt or arm protection you use be made of cotton because Rayon, polyester and some other synthetic materials can melt like wax or even burst into flame when brushed against a hot surface.

Since the injection molding machine operates at high temperatures, do not operate the machine in an area where there are combustible liquids, gases or vapors. Keep other combustible materials such as rags and paper items away from the machine as well.

Plastic injection molding can be a fun and safe hobby if caution is used. And people of all ages will be fascinated by how the machine works and items it produces. Remember small children like to touch things and their skin is much more tender than ours. It's your responsibility to prevent them from touching the hot surfaces on the machine. In fact, it is best they watch the operation from a safe distance.

INJECTING YOUR FIRST MOLD

Now that you have completed building your injection molding machine and made your first mold, I'm sure you're anxious to see if it all works. The following steps will take you through the process.

STEP 1: First you will need some plastics strips 3" to 4" long and 1/4" to 3/8" wide to feed the machine. The strips can be cut from a plastic milk bottle, oil can, soda bottle or other thermoplastic bottle or item. All plastic must be rinsed off and dried before putting it in the machine. No residue of any kind should be on the plastic when it is placed in the machine. Also remove any paper labels that may be on the plastic. For obvious reasons do not use bottles, containers or plastic items that have contained chemicals, insecticides or other harmful agents in your projects.

STEP 2: The mold must be tightly clamped together to prevent   plastic from coming out at the parting line and damaging the item being produced. See the photo in **figure 74**. As you can see in the photo, a C-clamp is used to clamp this mold. Later we will learn how to make a mold clamp that will be used especially for this purpose.

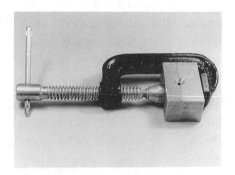

Fig. 74 "C"-clamp being used to hold mold together

STEP 3: The machine must be securely fastened to the surface of the work bench to prevent if from tilting forward when the injection lever is pulled. As you recall, holes were provided in the base rails for just this purpose.

STEP 4: Plug the machine into the GFI outlet and flip the switch on. The red indicator light should come on signaling that the machine is in operation. Adjust the thermostat to a midway position. The heater block will immediately begin to heat up. Most likely you will be using polyethylene plastic and its molding temperature is around 375-400 degrees. Keep an eye on the thermometer and adjust the thermostat accordingly. Depending on the type of plastic you are using, the melting temperature can vary so careful attention is required. Keep in mind that the thermometer only reads the surface temperature of the heater block. There is a heat loss factor between the surface of the heater block and the inside of the injection cylinder that you should be aware of. For instance your outside temperature may say 300 degrees when the inside temperature is really 400 degrees. After a while you will learn to compensate for this. A good rule of thumb is that if you see smoke coming off the plastic at any time, turn down the thermostat because the temperature is too high. It's also a good

Fig. 75 Feeding plastic strips into the injection cylinder

91

idea to keep a record of your melts and the temperature shown on the thermometer at the time you shot plastic into the mold. This is really the value of the thermometer because it gives you a reference number. Some of the items you produce may not turn out very well and this information will help in solving problems.

STEP 5: Insert the plastic strips into the cylinder as shown in **figure 75**. A very small screwdriver is handy for poking stubborn pieces in. Just be careful not to scratch the cylinder walls. Periodically pull down on the injection lever until you see a little bit of plastic ooze out of the injector tip. This compresses the plastic in the cylinder and allows you to add more.

STEP 6: While the plastic is heating up in the cylinder, set the mold on the adjustable table with the sprue aligned with the injector tip on the heater block. Raise the table until the sprue opening is forced tight against the injector tip. See **figure 76**.

Continue to monitor the temperature of the plastic. When it reaches 375-400 degrees it should be ready to inject. I have found that at the point the plastic begins to bulge or expand out of the top of the injection cylinder it is ready to inject. Remember, if there is smoke coming off the plastic it is probably too hot. You can burn plastic just like you can burn toast or anything else for that matter.

Fig. 76 Mold being held tight against the injector tip and ready to be injected with plastic.

STEP 7: Pull the injection lever down in a single, rapid and smooth motion to fill the mold with plastic. Do not stop until the injection lever meets a point of solid resistance. This point of solid resistance means that the mold is full. Hold the lever in position for 30-45 seconds. This gives the plastic a chance to solidify in the mold. Do not try to force the injection lever beyond the point of solid resistance because it is possible to bend the injector piston. I know because it happened to me. Luckily the piston is an easy part to make.

Fig. 77 Push down on the linkage with your thumb while pulling forward on the injection lever.

When the mold has solidified, raise the lever, lower the adjustable table and remove the mold from the table. Once in a while the linkage will lock up preventing you from beginning the pull down motion. This can be remedied by pushing down slightly on the linkage with your thumb as you begin pulling the injection lever. See the photo in **figure 77.**

STEP 8: Allow the mold to cool for a couple of minutes then loosen the C-clamp and separate the mold halves. You will be able to clearly see the molded plastic sprue running down to the gate that is connected to the two plastic slugs. Pry the two plastic slugs out of the mold with a small screwdriver placed under the gate. You can also pull them out by grabbing the sprue with a pair of pliers.

TROUBLESHOOTING

MOLD CAVITY DID NOT COMPLETELY FILL WITH PLASTIC: This is called a *short shot* and there are a couple of possible reasons for it occurring. When the hot plastic hits the cold surface of the mold cavity it solidifies very quickly. If you do not inject the plastic into the mold fast enough or if you stopped pulling the injection lever before the mold cavity was full, the charge would solidify prematurely.

Another possible cause for this occurrence is that the plastic did not reach its proper mold temperature. Check your records to see what the temperature of the plastic was when you injected it into the mold. Add 10 or 20 degrees to that temperature and try again.

PLASTIC SQUEEZES OUT OF THE MOLD AT THE PARTING LINE: This is called *flash* and it means that the mold was not clamped together tight enough. It can also mean that mating surfaces of the mold halves are uneven.

THE MOLD CAVITIES ARE FILLED COMPLETELY, BUT THERE ARE SHRINK CAVITIES IN THE CENTER OF EACH PART: This means that you did not keep pressure on the injection handle for a long enough period of time after the shot was complete.

PLASTIC SQUEEZES OUT BETWEEN THE SPRUE AND THE INJECTOR NOZZLE: Raise the table a little more to force the mold tighter against the injector nozzle.

A KNOB MOLD FOR THE ADJUSTABLE TABLE

We need a knob for the adjustable table. Making one will be a wonderful first project and it will give you an idea of what can be accomplished with the injection molding machine.

A photo of the mold and the knob you will be making is shown in **figure 78**. This will be a typical two part mold with the sprue centered at the parting line.

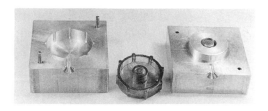

Fig. 78   **Knob and mold**

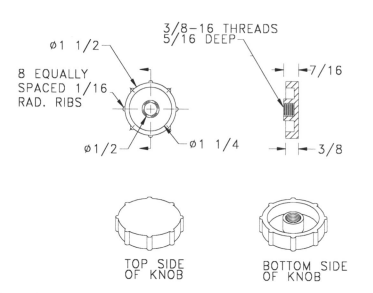

Fig. 79 **Drawing of the knob used on the adjustable table**

95

A drawing of the knob and its dimensions is shown in **figure 79**. Study the drawing carefully and see if you can come up with your own mold design. It's good practice. At first glance the ribbed edge on the knob may look intimidating but it's very simple to accomplish in the mold. This project will also show how easy it is to mold internal threads. It's a fun item to make and machining the mold is very simple. The finished knob turns out so nice and looks so professional it will be hard to believe you made it yourself and your friends won't believe it either. You will have to show them how it's done.

The material needed to make the mold is as follows.

Two pieces of 1" x 2-1/2" x 2-1/2" C.R.S. or aluminum bar stock.

One, 3/8-16 x 3/4" cap screw.

Two, 1/8" x 1/2" pieces of C.R.S. round rod for alignment pins.

Prepare the mold blanks by cutting off 2 pieces of 1" x 2-1/2" x 2-1/2" aluminum or cold roll steel bar stock. Face of both ends of each blank.

The layout for the top mold half is shown in **figure 80**. Center the blank in the 4-jaw chuck. Center drill and then drill through with a 5/16" drill bit.

Turn the end of the mold blank to 1-1/4" diameter, 1/4" back from the end.

Mount a boring bar in the tool post and bore to 1/2" diameter 5/16" deep. Remove and recenter the mold blank in the 4-jaw to work from the opposite end. Counter bore 9/16", 3/8" deep, then tap through 3/8-16.

Remove the mold half from the lathe. Locate and drill the two 7/64" holes through the mold half for the guide pins.

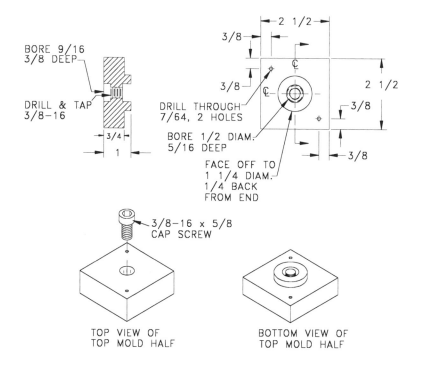

Fig. 80 Top half of knob mold, made from 1" x 2-1/2" x 2-1/2" aluminum or C.R.S bar stock

The top mold half is now complete and we can begin working on the bottom half shown in **figure 81.**

The first step is to scribe the 1-1/2" diameter circle centered on the face of the mold blank. Divide the circle into eight equal sections and mark the divisions with a center punch. Set the drill stop for the 3/8" depth and drill the eight 1/8" holes 3/8" deep.

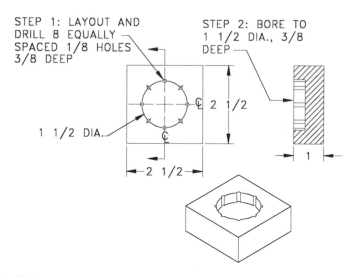

STEP 1: LAYOUT AND
DRILL 8 EQUALLY
SPACED 1/8 HOLES
3/8 DEEP

STEP 2: BORE TO
1 1/2 DIA., 3/8
DEEP

1 1/2 DIA.

2 1/2

2 1/2

1

Fig. 81 **Bottom half of knob mold, made from 1" x 2-1/2" x 2-1/2" aluminum or C.R.S. bar stock.**

Center the mold blank in the 4-jaw chuck and bore 1-1/2" 3/8" deep. The photo in **figure 82** shows the boring operation.

The procedure for drilling the holes in the bottom mold half for guide pins is the same as was used in the mold for the plastic slugs. I will go through the procedure again, but if you have questions you can refer to the drawings in **figure 69 and 71**. The 7/64" holes in the top

Fig. 82 **Boring the bottom mold half.**

mold half are used as a template for locating and drilling the 7/64" holes into the bottom mold half. The two mold halves are placed together and secured in the drill vise making sure they remain together and aligned. Set the drill stop for the depth necessary and drill the 7/64" holes 1/4" deep in the bottom mold half.

Separate the mold halves and ream the 7/64" holes in the top mold half with a .126" chucking reamer. Ream the 7/64" holes in the bottom mold half with a .124" chucking reamer. Make a set of guide pins as shown in **figure 70 on page 86.** Press them into the .124 reamed holes in the bottom mold half.

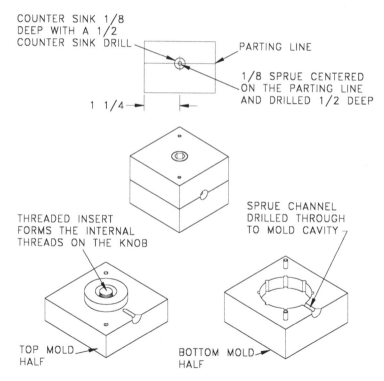

Fig. 83 **Locating and drilling the sprue in the knob mold**

Put the two mold halves back together. Locate the position for the 1/8" sprue. It will be centered on the parting line and it does not matter which side of the mold the sprue is located on. You can use a drill press to drill the sprue hole 1/2" deep. Or you can center the mold in a 4-jaw chuck and drill the sprue hole using the lathe tail stock chuck. Counter sink the sprue opening 1/8" deep with a 1/2" counter sink. See **figure 83**.

MAKING A CLAMP FIXTURE

There is a lot of pressure exerted on molds during the injection molding process. If the molds are not held tightly together they will split at the parting. The C-clamp we used in last job was able to hold our small slug mold together. But it will not be adequate for the knob mold or for that matter the rest of the mold projects in this book.

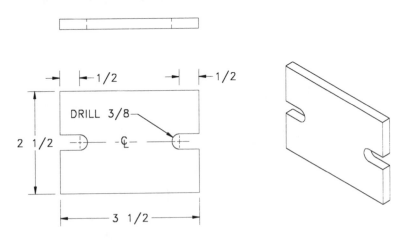

Figure 84 **End plates for clamping fixture made from 1/4" x 2-1/2" C.R.S. flat bar 3-1/2" long. Make 2.**

The clamp fixture will only take a few minutes to make. It consists of two end plates, two 6" lengths of 3/8-16 threaded rod and four 3/8-16 nuts with flat washers. Make each end plate from 1/4" x 2-1/2" x 3-1/2" C.R.S. flat bar. **See figure 84**. Locate and drill the 3/8" holes located 1/2" back from each end of each plate. Cut out the 3/8" slots in each end with a bandsaw or hacksaw.

Cut two, 6" lengths of 3/8-16 threaded rod, gather up four, 3/8-16 nuts and four, 3/8" flat washers and you have a clamping fixture. The drawing in **figure 85** shows how it works.

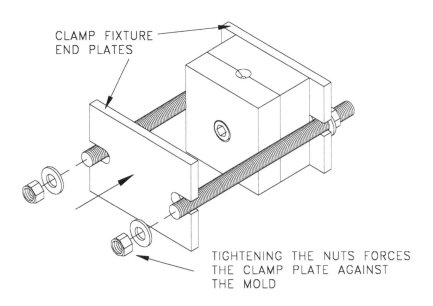

CLAMP FIXTURE
END PLATES

TIGHTENING THE NUTS FORCES
THE CLAMP PLATE AGAINST
THE MOLD

Fig. 85 Using the clamp fixture to clamp the knob mold.

INJECTING AND INSTALLING THE KNOB FOR THE ADJUSTABLE TABLE

The knob mold is complete and now we can prepare for the injection process. It is done in the same manner as was used for the plastic slug mold. Load the injection molding machine with plastic and turn the machine on. Of course you get to choose what color you want your knob to be. I wanted a black knob so I loaded the injection cylinder with plastic

Fig. 86 Mold on table.

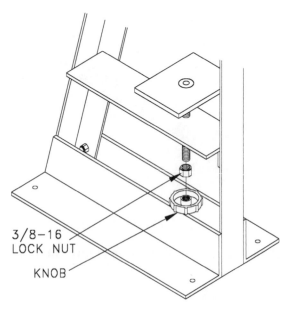

3/8-16
LOCK NUT

KNOB

Fig. 87   **Placing the knob on the adjustable table shaft.**

strips cut from a black plastic container.

With the clamp fixture holding the mold halves together, set the knob mold on the adjustable table. Align the sprue opening in the mold with the injector nozzle on the heater block. Raise the table to force the mold tight against the injector nozzle. Pull the injector lever to force plastic into the mold. Maintain pressure on the lever for a couple of minutes to allow the plastic to harden in the mold. Remove the mold from the machine and separate the mold halves. Unscrew the socket head screw from the top mold half and remove the finished knob.

The finished knob will mount to the screw shaft on the adjustable table as shown in **figure 87**. A 3/8-16 nut screws on the shaft with the knob. It is tightened against the knob to lock it in position.

MAKING A MOLD FOR A PLASTIC CONTAINER

This project will really show off the capabilities of the machine. The plastic container with snap on lid produced from these molds is impressive to say the least. It's a good one to show off too, because your friends will understand its purpose. Be careful how many people you show it to because everyone will want one.

Two molds will be required for this project. One for the plastic container and the other for the snap lid. We'll take them one at a time and begin by making the mold for the container. Before making the mold, study the drawing of the plastic container in **figure 88**. This will be a machining project much like the last mold we made and the material required to make it is as follows:

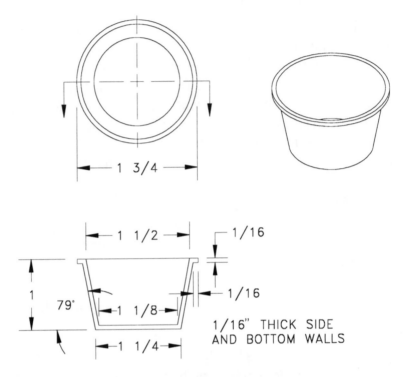

Fig. 88   **Small plastic container**

1" length of 2-1/2" x 2-1/2" aluminum or cold roll steel bar stock for the top half of the mold.

1-3/8" length of 2-1/2" x 2-1/2" aluminum or C.R.S. for the bottom half of the mold.

1-1/2" length of 1-1/2" aluminum or C.R.S. round rod for the plug insert.

One, 1/4-20 x 3/4" cap screw.

Two, 1/8" x 1/2" pieces of C.R.S. round rod for alignment pins.

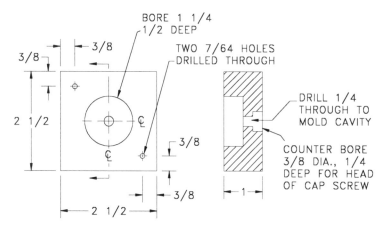

Fig. 89 Top mold half for plastic container. Made from 2-1/2" x 2-1/2" aluminum or C.R.S. bar stock.

A detailed drawing of the top mold section for the plastic container is shown in **figure 89**. Make it from a 1" length of 2-1/2" x 2-1/2" bar stock. Face off both ends of the mold blank. With the mold half centered in the lathe use the tail stock chuck to center drill, then drill 1/4" through. Mount a boring bar in the compound rest and increase the bore of the 1/4" hole to 1-

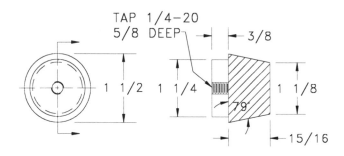

Fig. 90 Plug insert for top mold half. Made from 1-1/2" diameter aluminum or C.R.S round rod.

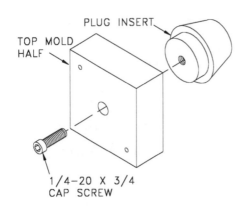

PLUG INSERT

TOP MOLD
HALF

1/4−20 X 3/4
CAP SCREW

Fig. 91 Assembling the top mold half.

1/4" diameter, 1/2" deep.

Remove the blank from the chuck. Turn it end for end and recenter it in the 4-jaw chuck. Counter bore the 1/4" hole to 3/8" diameter 1/4" deep.

This mold has a plug insert made from a 1-3/8" length of 1-1/2" diameter round rod. Place the blank in the 3-jaw chuck of the lathe. Face off both ends of the blank. Finished length to be 1-5/16". Using the tail stock chuck, center drill, then drill with a #7 drill 1/2" deep. Tap 1/4-20, 1/2" deep. Turn the 1-1/4" shoulder 3/8" back.

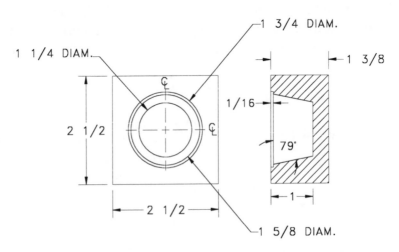

1 3/4 DIAM.

1 1/4 DIAM.

1 3/8

2 1/2

1/16

79°

2 1/2

1

1 5/8 DIAM.

Fig. 92 Bottom mold half machined from 1-3/8" x 2-1/2" x 2-1/2" aluminum or C.R.S. bar stock.

106

Fig. 93   **Mold and the container it produced.**

Remove the blank from the lathe. Turn it end for end and rechuck in the 3-jaw chuck. Adjust the compound rest to turn the 79-degree taper 15/16" back from the end.

Remove the plug insert from the lathe. Assemble the shouldered end of the insert to the mold half. The shouldered end will fit in the 1-1/4" diameter x 1/2" deep cavity of the mold half. Draw the plug down tight with a 1/4-20 x 3/4" cap screw. The assembly is shown in **figure 91**.

The bottom mold half is shown in **figure 92**. Begin by cutting a 1-3/8" length of 2-1/2" x 2-1/2" aluminum or C.R.S. bar stock. Face off both ends. Center the mold in the 4-jaw chuck. Using the tail stock chuck drill a 1/2" hole 1" deep. Mount a boring bar in the tool post and increase the diameter of the 1/2" hole to 1-1/4", 1" deep. Adjust compound rest to 79 degrees and bore the mold cavity 1" deep. Dimension at bottom of cavity to be 1-1/4". Dimension at the top of the cavity to be 1-5/8" diameter. Then bore to 1-5/8" diameter, 1/16" back from the end.

Fit the bottom mold half for guide pins just as you did in the other molds we have made. Clamp the mold halves together in the vise. Drill the 1/8" sprue opening centered on the parting line and through to the mold cavity. This is just as we have done in our other mold projects. If you have questions about fitting the guide pins or drilling the sprue hole refer to **pages 85 and 86.**

The injection procedure for the container is the same as that for the knob mold. Turn the injection molding machine on and load the cylinder with plastic strips. Clamp the mold halves together with the mold clamp and place the mold on the adjustable table. Align the sprue opening with the injection nozzle, raise the table and inject the mold.

I experienced a short shot problem with the first few attempts at injecting this mold and there is a good chance that you will too. By short shot I mean that the back side of the container mold did not fill with plastic. Short shots can be a real problem when injecting larger molds and molds with thin sections. See **figure 94** for look at a short shot. I was able to fix the problem by simply raising the molding temperature of the plastic by 20 degrees.

Fig. 94 Example of a short shot.

In some more complicated molds it may be necessary to preheat the mold or even vent the mold cavity to allow trapped air to escape. Preheating can be done in a small toaster oven. The mold can be vented by drilling a small 1/16" hole from the outside of the mold into the mold cavity. None of these procedures will be necessary for the molds we are making. But at some time you may come across a situation where simply raising the molding temperature of your plastic will not solve the problem.

108

A SNAP LID FOR THE PLASTIC CONTAINER

A drawing of the snap on lid for the plastic container is shown in **figure 95**. We will begin by making the top mold half. The material required to make the mold is as follows:

Two, 1" lengths of 2-1/2" x 2-1/2" aluminum or C.R.S. bar stock for the top and bottom mold half.

1" length of 1-7/8" aluminum or C.R.S. round rod for the plug insert.

One, 1/4-20 x 3/4" cap screw.

2 pieces of 1/8" diameter x 1/2" long C.R.S. round rod for the alignment pins.

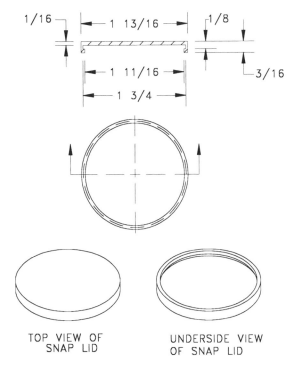

TOP VIEW OF
SNAP LID

UNDERSIDE VIEW
OF SNAP LID

Fig. 95   **Snap on lid for plastic container.**

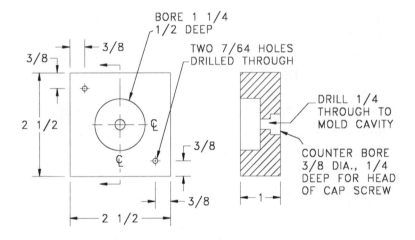

Fig. 96 **Top mold half for snap on lid, made from a 1"
length of 2-1/2" x 2-1/2" aluminum or C.R.S. bar stock.**

The top mold half for the snap lid is made exactly the same
as the top mold half for the container. The machining procedure
for making it will be the same too. The only difference between

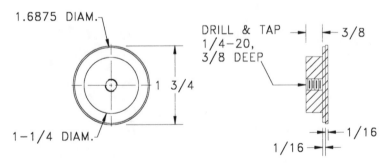

Fig. 97 **Plug insert for snap lid mold, made from a 1-1/2"
length of 1-7/8" aluminum or C.R.S. round rod.**

the two will be the length of the sprue channel. I have included the layout drawing again in **figure 96** so you won't have to flip back in the book to find it.

The mold for the snap lid has a plug insert too. See **figure 97**. Make it by cutting a 1-1/2" length of 1-7/8" round rod. Place the blank in the 3-jaw

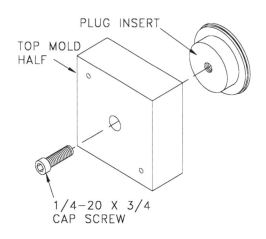

Fig. 98 **Assembling the top mold half.**

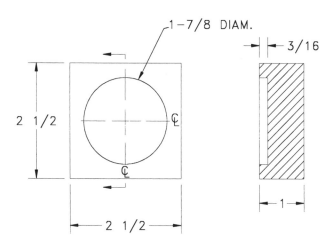

Fig. 99 **Bottom mold half for snap lid, made from 1" x 2-1/2" x 2-1/2" aluminum or C.R.S. bar stock.**

Fig. 100   Mold and the snap lid it produced

chuck of the lathe so that at least 3/4" sticks out past the jaws of the chuck. Face off the end. Using the tail stock chuck, center drill, then drill with a #7 drill 3/8" deep. Tap the #7 hole 1/4-20. Reduce the diameter of the blank to 1-3/4", 1/2" back from the end. Further reduce the diameter to 1-1/4", 3/8" back from the end. Turn the 1.6875" shoulder 1/16" back from the end. Finally part off the plug insert at 1/2" length.

Assemble the plug insert to the top mold half as shown in **figure 98**. The 1-1/4" shouldered end of the plug will fit inside the 1-1/4" diameter x 1/2" deep cavity in the mold half. Draw the plug down tight with the 1/4-20 x 3/4" cap screw.

The detailed drawing for the bottom half mold for the snap lid is shown in **figure 99**. This is one of the simplest mold halves we have made so far.

Make it from a 1" length of 2-1/2" x 2-1/2" aluminum of C.R.S. bar stock. Face off both ends of the mold blank. Center it in the 4-jaw chuck and bore the 1-7/8" diameter mold cavity 3/16" deep.

Remove the mold from the chuck and fit it for the guide pins just as we have done with our other molds.

Before drilling the sprue, remove the plug insert from the top mold half. Then put the mold halves back together and mark the location for the sprue hole which will be centered on the parting line. Center the mold halves in the 4-jaw chuck and drill the 1/8" sprue through to the mold cavity. Counter sink the sprue opening 1/8" deep with a 1/2" counter sink drill.

Install the mold insert, clamp the mold halves together, prepare the molding machine and inject the mold with plastic just as we have done before. A photo of the mold with the snap lid it produced is shown in **figure 100**.

CASTING MOLDS

Producing injection molds using the casting method makes it possible to duplicate parts. And casting is also a good way of producing a mold for items that would otherwise be difficult to machine. That is you would make a pattern of wood, plastic, or other material and then cast a mold of your pattern.

We will be talking about the casting process using *molding plaster of paris* as the molding medium. Another casting material that we will be discussing is *aluminum filled epoxy resin*. Both are thermoset materials.

Aluminum filled epoxy is a two-part system consisting of a liquid resin and a liquid hardener. The liquid hardener is added to the resin causing a chemical reaction and within a period of time the mixture cures and becomes hard. Cast epoxy is strong and gives good surface detail. The biggest draw back to using aluminum filled epoxy is its high cost. About $30.00 a pound at the time this book goes to press.

Molding plaster of paris is a good casting medium for beginners because it is much cheaper than epoxy. I decided to give it a try because I had a hard time justifying the expense of epoxy for simple experimental molds and much to my surprise it worked very well.

Before going any further we need to learn a little more of what casting is. The best way to do this is to explain the procedure. As·in all things, there are variations, but what we are going to discuss here is casting in its simplest terms.

Step 1: To begin, you need a pattern. The pattern can be an existing item you want to duplicate or it can be a pattern you have made. If you remember we discussed the issue of draft (the tapered sides of a pattern) earlier when we were machining molds. It is even more important when casting molds. You must be able to remove the pattern once the mold is cast. Sometimes it is necessary to divide the location of the pattern along the parting line. That is, place half the pattern in the drag and the other half of the pattern in the cope. For example, if you were to lay the pattern for a cylinder on the molding plate and fill the drag with epoxy resin you would find that it would be impossible to remove the cylinder pattern without damaging the mold. **Figure 101** illustrates this.

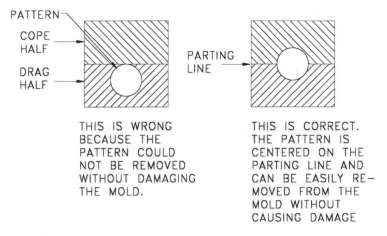

Fig. 101

You will also need a *pull pin* or *knock out pin* to aid in removing the pattern after the mold has cured. A pull pin is something attached to the pattern to aid in its removal. A knock out pin is part of the mold design. It's a small pin that extends from a flat surface of the mold cavity to the exterior of the mold. When the mold is cured the end of the knock out pin is hit with a hammer causing the pattern to pop out of the mold cavity. Knock out pins can also be used for removing finished plastic parts from an injection mold.

Step 2: The pattern is placed on a *mold plate*. The pattern and mold plate are coated with a *release agent*. A release agent is a coating designed to spoil the bond and make the pattern easy to remove from the mold cavity. For plaster molds the release agent is petroleum jelly (Vaseline). There are release agents specifically designed for aluminum filled epoxy that are commercially available.

A mold plate is a flat smooth surface usually a C.R.S. steel plate sized a little larger than the *flask*. Flasks are boxes with open ends and are used to contain the molding material. Flasks have two or more parts. The bottom half of the flask is called the drag. The top half is called the cope. A middle section (called a *cheek*) is only used when molding difficult shapes.

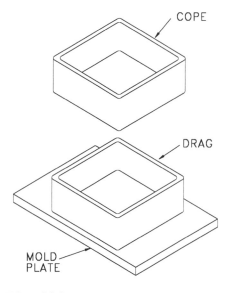

Fig. 102

Step 3: The drag portion of the flask is placed around the pattern. The molding medium (epoxy resin or plaster of paris) is poured into the drag to fill the mold half. The surface is struck off level and the mold is allowed to cure (harden).

Step 4: When cured, the drag is turned over and its surface is coated with a release agent. Then the cope is placed on top of drag and it too is filled with molding material. The surface is struck off level and the mold is allowed to cure.

Step 5: The flask is separated and the pattern is removed. If guide pins were not included as part of the mold they must be located and installed now. Procedure would be the same as in past molds we have made. The procedure for locating and drilling the sprue hole would also be the same as in past molds we have made.

Step 6: The mold is done. Clamp it together, prepare the injection molding machine and inject the mold.

USING EPOXY RESIN

Aluminum filled epoxy resin is easy to use and works very well for casting molds. It's a two-part system consisting of a liquid hardener and aluminum liquid resin. Mixing instructions and cautionary information come with the product. Using the epoxy is simply a matter of mixing it up and pouring it into the mold and waiting for it to cure, usually overnight.

Before using the epoxy, the pattern, mold plate and parting surfaces must be coated with a release agent. This is to prevent the epoxy from sticking to them. Using the right release agent is important because if the pattern sticks to the epoxy you will have ruined the mold and wasted several dollars. Patterns are harder to remove from epoxy molds than from plaster molds so be sure and have a securely attached pull pin mounted to the pattern or if necessary include a knock out pin as part of the mold.

Epoxy is strong and gives good surface detail, but as mentioned earlier it is expensive. And because of that it will be one of those items I seldom use around the home shop. Better to experiment with plaster of paris and save a few bucks. If you plan to use a mold more than a couple of times then consider using epoxy. Aluminum filled epoxy may be a tough item to find at the local level. I purchased my epoxy and release agent by mail order from "IASCO," Which stands for Industrial Arts Supply Co., 5724 West 36th Street, Minneapolis, MN 55416-2564. Phone 612-920-7393.

The brand I used was made by the Devcon Company, 30 Endicott Street, Danvers, MA 01923. Phone 508-777-1100. If you call them they can probably give you the names of distributors in your area.

USING MOLDING PLASTER OF PARIS

Molding plaster of paris is an inexpensive alternative to using aluminum filled epoxy. As a beginner it is much easier to mess up a plaster mold that costs only a few pennies than an epoxy mold that may cost as much as $30.00. Many of you will be skeptical about a plaster mold. But leaving the mold encased in a steel flask gives it the strength necessary to withstand the molding pressures. The product must be labeled molding plaster of paris. Other types of plaster such as those used for patching walls will not work. Molding plaster can be found in most hobby stores.

Of course you should be warned that a plaster mold will not last as long as one made from epoxy resin. Plaster tends to be brittle around the edges of the mold cavity. And chunks can easily chip away when removing finished parts. You will be lucky if you get more than 1 or 2 shots out of a plaster mold, but the cost of the plaster is so minimal that it is really the only way to learn how to produce molds using the casting method. Save the aluminum filled epoxy for those molds you plan to use a lot.

The release agent for plaster molds is Vaseline. It's simple to use and simple to find. I brush a thin coating on surfaces that I do not want the plaster to adhere to.

The catalyst for plaster is water and because of this the steel flask that encases the plaster mold will rust. This problem can be reduced by priming and painting all surfaces of the mold flask and using aluminum or stainless steel guide pins and inserts.

Another problem you will experience with plaster molds is air bubbles. These can form small craters on the surface of the mold cavity. This can be fixed and the surface of the mold can be sealed and strengthened by brushing a thin coat of epoxy over the surface of the mold cavity. We are talking about general purpose two-part epoxy and it can be found at most hardware stores at a modest cost. Follow the mixing instructions that come with the epoxy and mix a small amount in a metal container. If necessary, you can thin the epoxy to a brushable consistency by mixing in a small amount of lacquer thinner. Allow for plenty of ventilation when using lacquer thinner because the fumes are harmful. It is also a very flammable solvent so do your mixing away from those areas that could pose a fire threat.

CASTING A MOLD FOR A SMALL KNOB

A small knob is an ideal model for demon-
strating the reproduction of a part using the
casting method. That is, it's simple and small.
We are going to use molding plaster of paris
as the casting medium in this project.

The knob I am using for a pattern is one I
happened to find in the junk box. See **figure
103**. It's an appliance replacement knob and
is made from a thermoset material, probably *phenolic*. Phenolic
is a hard, rigid, heat resistant material. So keep in mind that I
am duplicating the shape of the knob and not its characteristics.
For instance, my knob will be made out of polyethylene which
could not survive the heat generated by some appliances. In
other words it could melt or soften. Also, the hard, rigid
characteristics of phenolic would make it a longer lasting
product in this application.

First you will need to make the mold plate as shown in
figure 104. It's a 1/4" x 3" x 4-1/2" piece of C.R.S. flat bar.
Drill 1/4" holes in the three locations shown. Two of the 1/4"

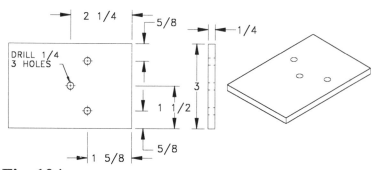

Fig. 104 **Mold plate, made from 1/4" x 3" x 4-1/2"
H.R.S.**

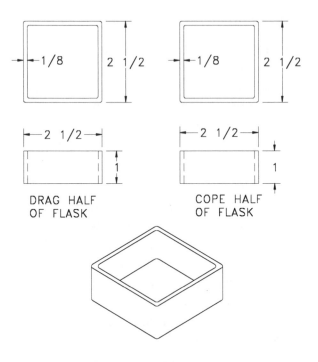

Fig. 105 Cope and drag, made from 2-1/2" x 2-1/2" x 1/8"
wall thickness. rectangular steel tube.

holes are for guide pins. The third 1/4" hole is for the insert
which will form the hole in the knob for the shaft. When you
are finished making the mold plate, place it on a flat surface.

The cope and drag halves of the flask are shown in **figure
105**. The cope and drag are each made from a 1" length of 2-
1/2" x 2-1/2" x 1/8" wall thickness, rectangular steel tube. The
flask must fit together evenly so it is best to face off both ends
of the cope and drag. It's also a good idea to primer and paint
the flask to prevent rust. Cut two, 1/4" diameter x 1/2" long
guide pins. Put a slight chamfer on the end of each guide pin. If

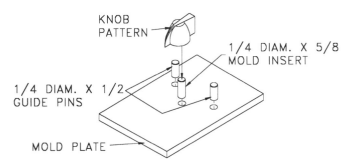

Fig. 106

you are making the mold with epoxy resin, C.R.S. guide pins will work fine. If using plaster of paris the guide pins should be made of aluminum or stainless steel to prevent rust.

Cut a 5/8" length of 1/4" round rod for the insert used to form the hole in the knob for the mounting shaft. Chamfer both ends of the insert. All knobs are not the same and what you are duplicating may require a different size, shape or length of insert. Place the insert in the knob and tighten the set screw. Tighten the set screw good and tight because the insert will also serve as our pull pin when we remove the pattern from the mold cavity. Cover the set screw hole in the knob pattern with a piece of tape or fill it with putty. Plumbers putty works good for this. The reason for covering the hole is to keep molding plaster from getting into it and ruining the mold when you attempt to remove the pattern.

Put the knob with insert into the hole provided for it in the mold plate as shown in **figure 106**. Then put the guide pins in their respective holes. Guide pins will extend 1/4" above the surface of the mold plate. Coat the pattern and mold plate with petroleum jelly. Do not get any on the guide pins because we want those to remain in the mold half.

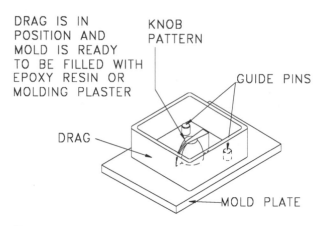

DRAG IS IN POSITION AND MOLD IS READY TO BE FILLED WITH EPOXY RESIN OR MOLDING PLASTER

KNOB PATTERN

GUIDE PINS

DRAG

MOLD PLATE

Fig. 107

Place the drag around the pattern as shown in **figure 107**. Mix up the molding plaster of paris following the instructions on the container. Pour to fill the mold half. Tamp down the mixture to remove any air pockets and using a straight edge strike the surface of the mold off level. Allow the mold to set up hard.

After the drag is cured, turn it over so that the pattern half is on top. Coat the parting surface, exposed pattern and guide pins with petroleum jelly. Set the cope on top of the drag. Fill it with molding plaster and strike off level and allow it to cure.

Separate the flask. Grab the knob insert with a pair of pliers and

Fig. 108 Mold ready for cope.

122

Fig. 109 **Mold and duplicate knob it produced**

carefully pull the pattern from the mold cavity.

The sprue will be centered on the parting line just as it has been in the other molds we have made. Drill the sprue with an 1/8" drill through to the mold cavity. Counter sink the sprue with a 1/2", 45 degree counter sink drill.

Before injecting the mold we need to make sure all the moisture has evaporated from the plaster. You can speed the process up by placing the finished mold in an oven for 15 or 20 minutes at 400 degrees. I keep a small toaster oven in my shop for just this purpose. When the mold has cooled you can coat the mold cavity with a thinned solution of epoxy. Any small pits that may exist on the surface of the cavity can be filled with epoxy as well.

I found that I could extend the life of my plaster molds and prevent plaster from adhering to the plastic by coating the mold cavity with a release agent before injecting it with plastic. Doing this also made the plastic parts easier to remove from the mold. You can use a commercial release agent or a very thin coating of petroleum jelly.

Your mold is done. Make sure the knob insert and guide pins are in positon. Clamp the mold together, prepare the injection machine and inject the mold.

CONCLUSION

Congratulations. Now that you have learned how to make and inject your own plastic molds anything is possible and what you produce will be limited only by your imagination. There are many useful items that can be produced with your machine and since you will be using recycled plastic, what you make will cost little more than the time it takes to make it. Keep notes about the characteristics and molding temperatures of the different plastics you use. You will find this to be a great help in deciding which plastic to use in a particular design. For instance, I found that items made from a plastic motor oil container were softer and more flexible than items made from clear plastic soda pop bottles. It's also a lot of fun to mix colors and produce interesting marble effects in your items.

Look at commercially produced plastic items and try to figure out what the mold may have looked like that made them. You can usually locate the parting line on these items and often tool and grinding marks from the mold will show up too. And chances are you can locate the area where the gate was trimmed away. These are all important secrets that will help in designing your molds.

As in any hobby or profession there are always new things to learn. And having just scratched the surface in this new and exciting hobby I am sure you will want to learn more. And the best way to learn is by doing. Start putting your ideas down on paper and don't be afraid to give them a try, after all, they're almost certain to work.

SOURCES

Plastic injection molding seems to be a hobby that has not entered the main stream. Because of that, sources of material and supplies are hard to find. If you happen to be a manufacturer, stuff is available, but only in large quantity lots. Since you will more than likely have a tough time finding a source for the cartridge heater and thermostat used in this project we thought it best to make them available to those of you who decide to build the machine. Ordering and price information are as follows.

Prices are in effect as of the publication date of this book, but they are subject to change. Call or write for current prices and shipping costs.

Order from: Gingery Publishing   Phone (417) 890-1965
             P.O. Box 318
             Rogersville, MO 65742

             Email: gingery@gingerybooks.com

Cartridge Heater: 120 volt, 250-watt cartridge heater. Measures 3/8" diameter X 3" long. Manufactured by Chromalox®. Part# CRP-203A025.
Price. . . . . $24.95 plus shipping

Thermostat: 120 volt adjustable thermostat. Adjusts from 250 to 600 degrees Fahrenheit. Comes with a black knob. Manufactured by Chromalox®. Part# SA-701A
Price . . . . . . $29.95 plus shipping

SOURCES

A good source for supplies to the plastic hobby market is **Industrial Arts Supply Company, 5724 West 36th Street, Minneapolis, MN 55416-2594. Phone 612-920-7393.** Their catalog costs $2.00 and they seem to cater mostly to schools and universities. I purchased my aluminum filled epoxy from them and they had a good buy on oven thermometers of the type used on our machine. They also have aluminum filled epoxy and mold release agents. They stock a variety of small hand operated injection molding machines and completed molds can be purchased from them as well. Keep in mind that the sprue opening on their molds may not match our machine, but it might be possible to modify the injector tip on our machine to fit their molds.

The brand of the aluminum filled epoxy I used is manufactured by the Devcon Company, 30 Endicott Street, Danvers, MA 01923. Phone (508) 777-1100. If you call them they will give you names of distributors in your area.

You probably won't have much trouble locating the angle and bar stock used to build the machine, but the 2-1/2" x 2-1/2" bar stock use to make the molds may be tough to locate. As I mentioned at the beginning of the book, check with your local steel supply house first. If you have problems finding it I have listed the names of some mail order companies that sell steel, brass and aluminum in rounds, flats, squares and angle. Addresses are as follows.

Blue Ridge Machinery & Tools, Box 536, Hurricane, WV 25526. Phone (304) 562-3538.

Campbell Tools, 2100 Selma Rd., Springfield, OH 45505. Phone (937) 322-8562.

SOURCES

Cardinal Engineering, Rt. 1 Box 163, Cameron, IL 61423. Phone (209) 342-7474.

Metal Buyers Mart, N15 W22218 Watertown Rd#3, Waukesha, WI 53186. Phone 800-657-0721.

For the names of other suppliers and to keep up to date on the metal working craft you might consider subscribing to a trade magazine such as **Home Shop Machinist**, Village Press Inc., P.O. Box 1810, Traverse City, MI 49685-1810.

BOOKS

Plastics Mold Engineering, Written by J.H. DuBois and W.I. Pribble. 5th edition published by Chapman and Hall in 1995. ISBN#0412989514 Library Of Congress #94-17065. It's a large and expensive book with about 700 pages covering all aspects of mold engineering. You might check with the library and see if they have a copy.

Do It Yourself Vacuum Forming, Written by Douglas E. Walsh. This is an interesting book that shows how to vacuum form plastic. Includes plans to make a vacuum forming machine and instructions on mold making. Book is available through **Lindsay Publications, P.O. Box 538, Bradley, IL 60915-0538. Phone (815) 935-5353.**